GENESIS TO JESUS

JOURNEY THROUGH SCRIPTURE

Participant Workbook

Writers: Matthew Leonard, Raquel Lopez, Emily Stimpson Chapman, Rob Corzine, Kimberly Hahn, Michael Barber, Curtis Mitch
Media/Print Production: Matthew Leonard, Raquel Lopez, Patty Borgman, Scionka INC, Alex Renn
Graphic Design: Patty Borgman

Acknowledgements: We sincerely thank all those whose generosity of time, talent, and treasure made this project possible.

St. Paul Center for Biblical Theology
1468 Parkview Circle
Steubenville, OH 43952

Front Cover Image: *Christ Rising from Tomb* – G. Ferrari
Photo Credit: Restored Traditions

Table of Contents

Welcome to Journey Through Scripture

Journey Through Scripture is the St. Paul Center's dynamic Bible study program designed to help ordinary Catholics grow in their knowledge of Scripture while deepening their understanding of the riches of our faith. Distinctively Catholic, Journey Through Scripture reads the Bible from the heart of the Church, considering both the Old and New Testaments and how they work together. It's grounded in history, yet it actively engages topics faced by today's Catholics. More than just an ordinary Bible study, it's biblical catechesis.

There are several Journey Through Scripture studies. This participant workbook is for the foundational study of the entire series, *Genesis to Jesus*, a twelve-part video series that surveys the principal covenants that God made with his people through figures such as Adam, Noah, Abraham, Moses, and David. It also shows how each of these covenants points forward to—and is fulfilled by—Jesus Christ and his Church. In *Genesis to Jesus*, participants will see a panoramic vision of salvation history and our place in this story.

Study Components

Genesis to Jesus is designed for both group and individual study. It contains five possible components, all of which can be ordered at JourneyThroughScripture.com.

❖ This Participant Workbook

❖ *Genesis to Jesus* Participant Workbook

❖ *Genesis to Jesus* DVD set

❖ *A Father Who Keeps His Promises* by Dr. Scott Hahn

READING SCRIPTURE WITH THE CHURCH

A Bible Study About the Bible

Understanding the Bible requires an understanding of its "plot." And the Bible's plot is the story of salvation history. It is the story of human salvation unfolding in history according to God's plan. You and I need to read the Bible from the heart of the Church if we are to make sense of the Scriptures and apply them to our lives as Catholics. This includes an understanding of *why* we should read them and *how* we should read them.

In *Genesis to Jesus* we'll study the divine covenants that God made with humanity in the course of salvation history. We'll focus on his Old Testament covenants with Adam, Noah, Abraham, Moses, and David, and then we'll see how each is fulfilled in the New Testament covenant that God makes with the world through Jesus Christ.

What We'll Cover in Lesson 1

Introduction
Matthew Leonard, host of the series

Themes covered

❖ *Why* and *how* should Catholics study the Bible?

❖ The Mass as the key to understanding Scripture

❖ Scripture as the inspired Word of God

❖ Salvation history as a two-part story

Scripture Verses Read in Lesson 1

❖ Luke 24:13–24

❖ Luke 24:31–35

❖ John 16:12–14

❖ 2 Timothy 3:16–17

❖ Galatians 4:4–5

Notes

_____
_____
_____
_____
_____
_____
_____
_____
_____
_____
_____
_____
_____
_____
_____
_____
_____
_____
_____
_____
_____
_____
_____
_____
_____
_____
_____

Review Questions

1. The Last Supper account, the Emmaus road account, and the Catholic celebration of the Mass share several features in common. What are these common elements?

_____

_____

_____

_____

2. Explain the relationship between the Holy Spirit and the Holy Scriptures.

_____

_____

_____

_____

3. What does it mean to say that Christianity is "a religion of the Word"? And why is it inaccurate to say that Christianity is "a religion of the Book"?

_____

_____

_____

_____

4. Explain the difference between *secular* history and *salvation* history.

_____

_____

_____

_____

Discussion Questions

1. Can you think of anything in this lesson that you've never considered before, or even heard before? If so, how might this new information impact your relationship with God and others?

_____

_____

_____

_____

2. Can you think of time in your life when you experienced a "burning heart"? Have you ever encountered Jesus in a personal way, perhaps like the disciples traveling to Emmaus? Feel free to share your thoughts with the group.

_____

_____

_____

_____

This Lesson's Memory Verse

"And their eyes were opened and they recognized him; and he vanished out of their sight. They said to each other, 'Did not our hearts burn within us while he talked to us on the road, while he opened to us the scriptures?'"

LUKE 24:3–32

Preparation for the Next Lesson

❖ *A Father Who Keeps His Promises* by Dr. Scott Hahn, ch. 1

❖ *Catechism of the Catholic Church*, paragraphs 112–114

❖ *Dei Verbum*, Vatican II Constitution on Divine Revelation stpaulcenter.com/deiverbum

THE OLD & THE NEW

Review of the Previous Lesson

A Bible Study About the Bible

Understanding the Bible requires an understanding of its "plot." And the Bible's plot is the story of salvation history. It is the story of human salvation unfolding in history according to God's plan. You and I need to read the Bible from the heart of the Church if we are to make sense of the Scriptures and apply them to our lives as Catholics. This includes an understanding of *why* we should read them and *how* we should read them.

The Emmaus Road

Luke's Gospel tells the story of two disciples who are traveling from Jerusalem to Emmaus on Easter Sunday. They are genuine believers in Jesus, but they are perplexed and discouraged by the events of Good Friday. Suddenly, they are joined by Jesus. Neither disciple recognizes who this "stranger" is until he begins to open the Scriptures to them. He explains that the Scriptures (the Old Testament) announce the coming of the Messiah,

and that is was necessary to God's plan that the Messiah should suffer before entering his glory. The two disciples are astounded and encouraged, yet they still don't recognize this stranger as the risen Jesus (Luke 24:13–35).

Drawing near to Emmaus, the disciples urge their traveling companion to stay with them. He agrees and joins them for a meal. At table Jesus *takes* bread, *blesses* it, *breaks* it, and then *gives* it to the disciples—actions that immediately call to mind the events of the Last Supper, when Jesus took, blessed, broke, and gave the consecrated food to the disciples (Luke 22:14–30). Now at last the disciples discover the Real Presence of Christ in their midst in the breaking of the bread, which is biblical language for the celebration of the Mass (Luke 22:31–35).

The Mass: The Key to the Bible

The Emmaus road story draws our attention to the role of the Scriptures and the Sacraments in the Christian life. Reading and interpreting the Scriptures caused the *hearts* of the disciples to burn, and the breaking of the bread caused their eyes to be opened. This is precisely what should happen to us during the celebration of every Mass: our hearts should be enflamed by Scripture, and our *eyes* should be opened to the presence of Christ in the Blessed Sacrament! Our worship offers us a personal encounter with the Word of God—the Word written as well as the Word made Eucharist.

The Bible is therefore a liturgical book. Its *content* is liturgical because it shows us God's people praying and worshipping the Lord by means of sacrifice and praise. Its *context* is also liturgical because its books were collected and preserved for the express purpose of being proclaimed in the liturgy. We see this in the pages of the New Testament, where the apostles instruct believers to read their writings before the congregation (e.g., Col 4:16; 1 Thess 5:27; Rev 1:3). This is the essential meaning of the expression: "reading the Bible from the heart of the Church."

Historically, there have been countless believers through the ages who never owned a personal copy of the Bible. Some lived before the Bible was a completed book. Others couldn't read. Still others lived before the invention of the printing press and could not afford a hand-written edition. Nevertheless, from the very beginning of the Church's history all believers had the opportunity to hear the Scriptures being proclaimed in the liturgy.

And notice that the Church reads from the *whole* Bible at Mass. We listen first to Old Testament readings from Moses and the Prophets, and then we listen to New Testament readings from the Gospels and the writings of the apostles. These readings prepare us to receive what the disciples traveling to Emmaus received: the Lord Jesus himself! When the priest *takes*, *blesses*, *breaks*, and *gives* the Eucharist to us, repeating the words of Jesus at the Last Supper, we are invited to recognize the risen Lord "in the breaking of the bread" (Luke 24:31, 35).

The Word Incarnate & the Word Written

Before Jesus ascended to the Father, he announced that "the Spirit of truth" was coming into the world to lead his disciples into "all the truth" (John 16:13). How does the Spirit do this? In two ways primarily: the Holy Spirit *inspires* the writing of Scripture, and then he *guides* the Church to understand the meaning of Scripture.

The *inspiration* of Scripture means that God is the principal author of the book. Human authors were involved in composing the biblical writings as well,

but the Spirit worked in and through them as they wrote, so that Scripture communicates the words of God in the words of men. Like Jesus himself, then, the Bible is both human and divine. Just as the Incarnate Word came into the world in a human nature without ceasing to be the divine Son, so the Inspired Word comes to us in human language without ceasing to be divine Speech. This is why the Church venerates the Bible just as she venerates the Body of the Lord.

The human authorship of Scripture means that the Bible is also a book of books. A variety of individuals living at different times in history contributed to the writing of Scripture, and they wrote in a variety of literary forms: prose, poetry, prophecy, proverb, apocalyptic vision, etc. More-over, it is clear from reading the Bible that the grace of inspiration did not suppress the personalities, talents, and perspectives of its human authors. So while the Scriptures are not *merely* human documents, they are *truly* human documents.

The *guidance* of the Spirit takes place in the Church, especially through the successors of the apostles—the pope and the bishops in union with him. This enables the Magisterium to be the "custodian" of the Word of God in all its forms, including the Scriptures. Relying on the Spirit's guidance, the Church's teaching authority is tasked with giving authentic interpretations of the Bible and with safeguarding the people of God against misunderstanding its message.

Salvation History

Unlike secular history, which restricts its focus to human actions and concerns, biblical history tells the human story from God's perspective, with its focus on divine actions and concerns. God's Word, then, is mainly about God's saving work. The Bible gives us nothing less than the drama of salvation history told from God's point of view!

Structurally, the Bible has two main parts: The Old Testament and the New Testament. The story of Scripture begins with creation (Gen 1:1) and ends with the glorious unveiling of a "new heaven" and a "new earth" at the end of time (Rev 21:1). At its center stands the cross of Christ. This means that salvation history is a two-part story. It's an account of God's *promises* before the coming of Jesus; and it's an account of God fulfilling those promises in the life, death, and resurrection of Jesus, so that all of human history *after* his coming is marked by the redemption he accomplished.

✪What We'll Cover in Lesson 2

<table>
<tr>
<td>

Themes Covered

❖ The use of "typology" in Scripture

❖ Scripture as a gift from God for the sake of our salvation

❖ The role of the Holy Spirit in relation to Scripture

❖ Salvation history as covenant history

</td>
<td>

Scripture Verses Read in Lesson 2

❖ John 6:31–35

❖ Psalm 119:9–11

❖ Deuteronomy 6:4–7

❖ 2 Thessalonians 2:15

❖ Ephesians 4:11–14

❖ Jeremiah 31:31–34

</td>
</tr>
</table>

Notes

Review Questions

1. Explain what is meant by the word "typology." How does typology reveal the unity of the Old and New Testaments?

_____

_____

_____

_____

2. How would you explain the difference between a covenant and a contract?

_____

_____

_____

_____

3. What does it mean to "read Scripture from the heart of the Church"?

_____

_____

_____

_____

Discussion Questions

1. Can you think of anything in this lesson that you've never considered before, or even heard before? If so, how might this new information impact your relationship with God and others?

_____

_____

_____

_____

2. Try to remember the last time you sat down and read the Bible on your own. What part of Scripture did you read? You are welcome (and encouraged) to share your experience.

_____

_____

_____

_____

3. Take a look at Psalm 119:9–11. How might committing parts of Scripture to memory affect your daily life?

_____

_____

_____

_____

This Lesson's Memory Verse

"All Scripture is inspired by God and profitable for teaching, for reproof, for correction, and for training in righteousness, that the man of God may be complete, equipped for every good work."

2 TIMOTHY 3:16–17

Preparation for the Next Lesson

❖ *A Father Who Keeps His Promises* by Dr. Scott Hahn, ch. 2

❖ *Catechism of the Catholic Church,* paragraphs 386–412

❖ *Dei Verbum,* Vatican II Constitution on Divine Revelation stpaulcenter.com/deiverbum

COVENANT WITH CREATION

Review of the Previous Lesson

Promise and Fulfillment

The Bible is a real book, a specimen of real literature. But it's not like any other book, or like any other literature. Its words function as literary signs pointing to historical realities, just as the words in other books do. But thanks to divine providence, even those historical realities outside the book are shaped by God into signs pointing to other realities—sometimes future realities, sometimes spiritual realities.

We might say that God writes the world—including the events of history—as men write words. He gives us concrete things that function as signs of greater things. For instance, the events of the Exodus prefigure the greater redemption that Christ accomplishes at a later point in history. Likewise, God raises up "savior figures" such as Noah, Moses, and David as foreshadowings of *the* Savior, Jesus Christ. The *Catechism* teaches as much when it states: "thanks to the unity of God's plan, not only the text of Scripture but also the realities and events about which it speaks can be signs" (CCC 117). So the people and events of the Old Testament signify in a prophetic way the Redeemer and the saving mysteries of the New Testament.

Saint Augustine captured this truth in a memorable way when he said that the New Testament *lies hidden* in the Old, and the Old Testament is *unveiled* in the New. What he recognized was the overarching unity of Scripture, a unity that is confirmed and brought to light by typology. He insisted, in concert with the apostles and Fathers of the Church, that Christ is foreshadowed in the Old Testament by a variety of "types."

This works out in a number of different ways. For example, just as an unblemished lamb was offered as the Passover sacrifice in the Old Testament, so also the sinless Jesus is sacrificed as "our paschal lamb" in the New Testament (1 Cor 5:7). Likewise, just as God fed his people in the wilderness with manna, which was miraculous bread from heaven, so also the Father feeds his flock with the humanity of Jesus, "the true bread from heaven" (John 6:32). Furthermore, the New Testament refers to the sacrificial system of the Mosaic law as a "shadow" of Jesus offering his life as the definitive sacrifice for sin (Heb 10:1). Numerous other examples of typology will be pointed out in the course of this study.

In essence, typology discerns the works of God in the Old Testament as signs fulfilled in the person of Jesus in the New Testament (CCC 128). Typology also reveals that the meaning of the events of the Old Testament is "inexhaustible" (CCC 129) and that they follow a gradual but "dynamic" movement toward the fulfillment of the Father's plan in the New (CCC 130).

The really exciting part of this truth applies to you and me. We as Christians are not simply spectators looking on from the outside as the Lord accomplishes his saving work in others. Nor are we merely students of his saving work in the past. On the contrary. We are *participants* in God's plan of saving the world. We stand in the same "stream" of salvation history as our biblical forebears—from Abraham and Moses and David to Mary and Joseph and the apostles!

The Bible: A Gift from God

The Bible is a treasure to be valued and shared. You might compare it to a family heirloom that is handed down from one generation to the next. Scripture's value rests mainly on this fact: it was written down "to instruct you for salvation" (2 Tim 3:15). By means of Scripture, the Lord bends down and speaks to us on a *human* level, but with the purpose of raising us up to a *divine* level through his grace.

In effect, the Bible takes the guesswork out of our efforts to please God and live as his children. It teaches that our lives are under the sovereign authority of God's Word, and so it instructs us in matters of family life, social life, personal life, and, of course, our spiritual life.

The Holy Spirit and Scriptural Interpretation

Saint Paul writes to an early Christian community in northern Greece: "So then, brethren, stand firm and hold to the traditions which you were taught by us, either by word of mouth or by letter" (2 Thess 2:15). By saying "word of mouth," Paul urges his readers to observe to all that he taught them orally and in person. By specifying "letter," he directs them to follow his written instructions sent on a previous occasion. Notice that Paul underlines the authority of both *oral* and *written* tradition.

Still, having oral and written instruction from the apostles is not enough. We also need reliable interpretation. After all, misinterpretation is a real danger. Thankfully, the Catholic Church not only preaches God's Word, she also gives a faithful interpretation of that Word. The Holy Spirit guides and empowers the Church's teaching authority—the bishop of Rome and the bishops of the world united with him—to proclaim and preserve the full revelation of God (CCC 100).

This full revelation, which forms a single deposit of the Word of God, comes to us in Sacred Scripture as well as Sacred Tradition (*Dei Verbum* 10). Scripture is the living and dynamic Word because God is its principle Author. Tradition, for its part, transmits an authentic understanding of God's living and dynamic Word, especially in the liturgy. The Holy Spirit directs and oversees the whole process, from inspiring the Scriptures to preserving its message in the Church.

Salvation History Is Covenant History

Saint Irenaeus, one of the ancient Fathers of the Church, recommends that we study the story of salvation in terms of its major covenants. "Understanding," he says, "consists in . . . showing why there are a number of covenants with mankind, and in teaching what is the character of each of the covenants" (*Against Heresies* 1.10.3).

We first need to see that the Old and New Testaments point us to the Old and New Covenants. In fact, a "testament" is what an ancient Israelite would call a "covenant." Salvation history unfolds and progresses as a sequence of covenants between God and his people.

People often think that covenants are no different than contracts. This is a misunderstanding, however. It is true that covenants and contracts both form *relationships* between people, but the *kind* of relationship created is very different. A covenant is much more than a contract, and it's important to understand how.

Contracts are made with a *promise* that is made and signed in *one's own name*, while covenants are made with an *oath* that is sworn in *God's name*. Likewise, contracts exchange *goods and services* and establish *temporary* relationships, whereas covenants involve an exchange of *persons* and create *permanent* relationships. In fact, covenants create family or kinship bonds. You might say the difference between a covenant and a contract amounts to the difference between marriage and prostitution! When God creates a covenant with us, then, he is inviting us into his family. He is our Father precisely because he brought us into his covenant and made us his children (CCC 238).

The first of God's covenants was made with Adam and Eve as *husband and wife*. The second was made with Noah and the family that formed his *household*. The third was established with Abraham as the chieftain over an entire *tribe* of people. The fourth was made with Moses, who served as a leader and judge over the twelve tribes of the *nation* of Israel. The fifth was made with David, who reigned with royal authority over the *kingdom* of Israel. The final covenant was made through Jesus Christ, who announced kingdom of God as the *worldwide* community of God's people. Salvation history thus reaches its climax in Christ and the Church. Through the proclamation of the gospel, all nations are reconciled to God and gathered into his covenant family.

This means that salvation history stretches beyond biblical history. It's something that is still unfolding in our midst. You and I are caught up into the same "flow" of God's mission to save the world that washed over the great figures of the Bible!

☺What We'll Cover in Lesson 3

Themes Covered

❖ The two creation accounts

❖ The human race created in God's image and likeness

❖ The Sabbath as a sign of God's creation covenant

❖ Adam as the high priest of humanity

❖ Marriage as a sign of God's covenant of love

Scripture Verses Read in Lesson 3

❖ Luke 3:38

Notes

Review Questions

1. How is the creation of the world similar to the building of the tabernacle and the temple?

_____

_____

_____

_____

2. How does Genesis describe the person and role of Adam?

_____

_____

_____

_____

3. What is the sign in creation that reveals the mystery of who God is?

_____

_____

_____

_____

Discussion Questions

1. Can you think of anything in this lesson that you've never considered before, or even heard before? If so, how might this new information impact your relationship with God and others?

_____

_____

_____

_____

2. Take a moment and read Genesis 1:26–28. How would you explain the statement that man and woman are fashioned in God's "image"? How do we reflect or "image" God in human life?

_____

_____

_____

_____

3. What would you say to someone who insists that the stories of creation in Genesis are not scientific?

_____

_____

_____

_____

This Lesson's Memory Verse

> "Then God said, 'Let us make man in our image, after our likeness; and let them have dominion over the fish of the sea, and over the birds of the air, and over the cattle, and over all the earth, and over every creeping thing that creeps upon the earth.'"
>
> ✠
>
> GENESIS 1:26

Preparation for the Next Lesson

❖ *A Father Who Keeps His Promises* by Dr. Scott Hahn, ch. 3

FALL FROM GRACE

Review of the Previous Lesson

In the Beginning

The first two verses of Genesis tell us that God brought the entire world into existence at the dawn of history. But he not only creates the world, he forges a covenant with the world. We hear of this in later passages such as Jeremiah 33:25, where the prophet speaks of the Lord's "covenant with day and night." God did not create the human family because he was lonely. God himself, being Father, Son, and Spirit, is *already a family*. He created us in order to draw us into his divine family.

Many people like to drag the creation accounts in Genesis into a "religion versus science" debate. But this is to miss the point of their message. Genesis 1 was written to tell us *why* God created the world, not *how* he went about it. Creation is the act of a loving God who made us for himself. The Catholic Church does not require us to hold either that God fashioned the world in a succession of six twenty-four

days or to believe in the theory of evolution. What we must believe is that God created the world out of nothing and that he created the first human couple in a state of original innocence and justice before they fell from his grace through sin.

Genesis describes the work of creation in terms of divine speech. Each time God says, "let there be," new realities burst into existence. When God speaks his powerful word, things happen. In the New Testament, we discover that God's word is more than a power—it's a divine Person: God the Son! Jesus is the divine Word of God through whom all things were made (John 1:1–3; Heb 1:2).

One of the keys to the creation account can be found in Genesis 1:2, which says that the world in the beginning was "without form and void." God addresses this problem, first, by forming the world into distinct *realms*, and second, by filling the void with *rulers*. The work of each day is followed by God's declaration that his work is "good" (Gen 1:4, 10, 18, 21, 25). But following the work of the sixth day, the day when man and woman are made, God declares that his creation is "very good" (Gen 1:31).

Moreover, we are told that man and woman are made in God's "image and likeness" (Gen 1:26–27). What exactly does this mean? An important clue can be found in Genesis 5:1–3, which recounts how Adam was made in the image of God, but which goes on to say that Adam's son, Seth, was made in the image and likeness of his father Adam. This implies that "image" and "likeness" designate sonship. Adam, bearing the image of his Creator, is thus described as "the son of God" (Luke 3:38).

The Sabbath

Following the work of creation in six days, God designates the seventh day as a day of rest (Gen 2:2). Initially this might strike us as odd. If God is infinitely powerful, why does he need to rest? Actually, he

doesn't. God is giving us something that *we* need. The Lord blesses and sanctifies the seventh day as a gift to man and woman. It is set apart as a holy day of rest from *our* work; it is a call for *us* to enter each week into a time of holy worship.

The seventh day also seals the covenant that God makes with creation. And since covenants are made by swearing an oath, it is significant that the Hebrew word for swearing an oath is *sheba* [sheh-váh], which can be translated "to seven oneself." The covenant with creation is thus revealed through the structure of the seven days. The seventh day, later called the Sabbath, is the sign of this covenant (see Exodus 31:16–17).

The Sabbath, which is the climax of the creation account, signifies that God calls man and woman to something far more glorious than *ruling* creation. They have a higher calling: *worshipping* the Creator of it all. The world is designed as a place for worship in addition to work. It is a holy place—a sanctuary—where the Lord is present and where you and I can enjoy covenant communion with the living God.

This vision of creation as a sanctuary is made more explicit in other passages of Scripture. When God describes the work of creation to Job, he describes it as the construction of a building (Job 38:4–11). When Solomon builds the Temple in Jerusalem, he mimics the original creation in seven days: he builds it in seven years, consecrates it in the seventh month of the year, inaugurates its services during a seven-day festival, and offers seven petitions on the occasion (1 Kings 6–8).

Two Creation Accounts

Genesis 1 and 2 presents us with two accounts of creation. But these two accounts are not in conflict. Rather, they function as two complementary accounts that draw our attention to different things. For instance, Genesis 1 depicts God as the sovereign *Creator* fashioning the universe into a cosmic temple for his presence. Genesis 2, however, depicts God as a *Father*. He attends to the most intimate details of man's creation and need for companionship.

The depiction of Adam in Genesis 2 is that of a king, priest, and firstborn son. He appears as the high priest of the human family. In ancient Israel, the father or patriarch of a large family served as a priest and leader of worship on behalf of his household. This priestly prerogative passed to his firstborn son, who inherited his father's authority and responsibilities. Adam assumed this role in the beginning as a royal firstborn son. Jesus, the new Adam, succeeds in this role where Adam failed and calls the Church to participate in his mission as a "royal priesthood" (1 Pet 2:9; cf. Rev 1:6).

Finally, if Genesis 1 shows us that God established a covenant *with* creation, Genesis 2 shows us that God also created a covenant *within* creation. Man and woman are made for a covenant relationship with the Lord, and they are made for a covenant union with each other. The two are joined as husband and wife in the primordial covenant of marriage.

On one level, God creates marriage to be a sign of his love for us. On another, he creates marriage to be a sign of his very Self. Marriage, which produces natural families, is an image of God's inner life as a divine family. The communion of Persons in the Trinity is thus reflected in the human fathers, mothers, and children of the world.

Temptation and Fall: Making Sense of the Story

There are several things to keep in mind when we turn to the story of man's temptation and fall. The *Catechism* tells us (1) that the biblical account of the Fall in Genesis 3 uses "figurative language" (2) that it affirms "a primeval event" that took place at the beginning of human history, and (3) that this inspired narrative "gives us the certainty of faith that the whole of human history is marked by the original fault freely committed by our first parents" (CCC 390). So the account in Genesis 3 is written more like poetry than a journalistic report, and yet it recounts an actual event—the original fault of Adam and Eve—that stains the rest of human history.

Turning to this account, we note that God alerts Adam and Eve to a possible *danger*. Adam, we recall, was charged with keeping (i.e., guarding) the garden (Gen 2:15). This implies the existence of a threat, of someone or something that he must guard it from. Likewise, the Lord places a *restriction* on Adam's freedom: he's allowed to eat from any tree of the garden except one—the tree of the knowledge of good and evil. Finally, God issues a solemn *warning* to Adam: if he disobeys the divine command and chooses to eat from the forbidden tree, he will die that very day (Gen 2:17). For this warning to have any force or meaning, Adam must have understood something about death and found it dreadful.

One last thing should be kept in mind as well. When the Lord breathes life into the first man, Adam, he gives him something special that is *not* given to the plants and animals around him (Gen 2:7). Adam is given the grace of divine sonship. He receives his natural life from God, yes; but he also receives supernatural life. This is a way of saying that Adam and Eve are created in a state of grace (CCC 375). It means that, before the Fall, they live in harmony with the Lord, with each other, and with the rest of creation. They are neither simple-minded nor inclined to sin. On the contrary, they are upright, intelligent, and united in fellowship with God.

What We'll Cover in Lesson 4

Themes Covered

❖ The temptation and sin of Adam of Eve

❖ The covenant curses after the Fall

❖ Jesus as the New Adam

❖ God's plan of mercy

Scripture Verses Read in Lesson 4

❖ Genesis 2:15–17

❖ Genesis 3:1–6

❖ Genesis 3:9–13

❖ Romans 5:17–19

❖ Hebrews 2:14–15

Notes

_____
_____
_____
_____
_____
_____
_____
_____
_____
_____
_____
_____
_____
_____
_____
_____
_____
_____
_____
_____
_____
_____
_____
_____
_____
_____

Review Questions

1. Where does God's first promise of a Savior appear in Scripture? What does it tell us?

_____

_____

_____

_____

2. Take a moment and read Romans 5:12–21. Explain how Saint Paul compares and contrasts the first man, Adam, and Jesus, the new Adam.

_____

_____

_____

_____

3. After the Fall, God shows himself merciful to Adam and Eve in two specific ways. What are these two merciful provisions?

_____

_____

_____

_____

Discussion Questions

1. Can you think of anything in this lesson that you've never considered before, or even heard before? If so, how might this new information impact your relationship with God and others?

_____

_____

_____

_____

2. What do the failings of Adam and Eve tell us about the struggle of men and women to live as sons and daughters of God?

_____

_____

_____

_____

3. Where do you see the curses of the covenant—the consequences of Adam and Eve's sin—manifest in the world today?

_____

_____

_____

_____

This Lesson's Memory Verse

"I will put enmity between you and the woman, and between your seed and her seed; he shall bruise your head, and you shall bruise his heel."

✚

GENESIS 3:15

Preparation for the Next Lesson

❖ Genesis 4–11

❖ *A Father Who Keeps His Promises* by Dr. Scott Hahn, ch. 4

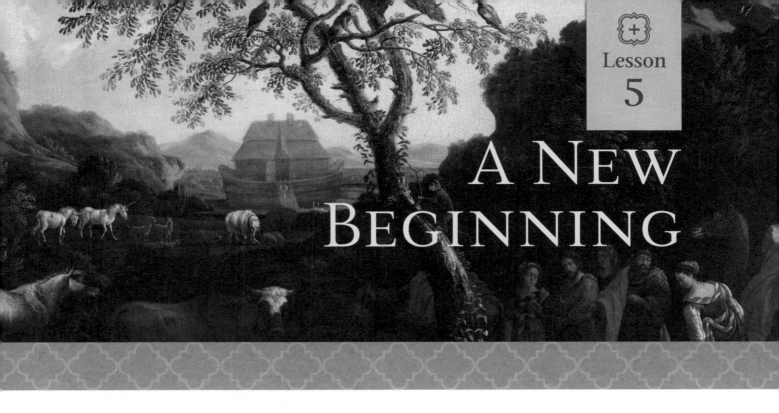

A New Beginning

Review of the Previous Lesson

Along Came a Serpent

Everybody's seen paintings of the temptation of Adam and Eve in the garden. Typically, the serpent appears as a long, slithering creature coiled around the branch of an apple tree. We should be aware, however, that the Hebrew word for "serpent," *nahash* [nuh-hásh], may suggest a deadlier creature than a slimy garden snake. Elsewhere in the Bible the term *nahash* can refer to far more dreadful and lethal creatures (e.g., Num 21:6–9; Isa 27:1–3). Viewed against this background, we can see that Adam, who is charged with guarding the garden, faces a serious threat to himself and his wife (CCC 395).

The serpent initiates a dialogue with Eve, but he is also speaking to Adam. We know this because the Hebrew word for "you" is plural in Genesis 3:1, 4–5. The serpent openly contradicts the word of God that threatens death if Adam eats from the forbidden tree: "You will not die" (Gen 3:4). The temptation, then, is a test of obedience and faith.

The test set before Adam is fourfold. (1) As a *son*, will Adam trust in the goodness of the Father and obey his word? (2) As a *king*, will Adam exercise his royal authority over the animals and expel the serpent from the garden? (3) As a *husband*, will Adam rise up as the protector of his new bride? (4) As a *priest*, will Adam sacrifice himself—if necessary—out of love for his wife and obedience to his Lord? In other words, will Adam fear the loss of his natural human life more than he fears losing the greater blessing of supernatural life?

As we know, Adam fails in his duties. Having allowed his trust in God to expire, and having failed to guard the garden, he allows the serpent to gain entrance. Adam should have rebuked the lying serpent, and yet he remained *silent*. And instead of leading his wife into righteousness, he follows her lead in committing sin. Adam prefers himself to his Creator and refuses to offer himself in obedience to God (CCC 397–398).

God Confronts Adam and Eve

Once the sin is committed, God comes looking for Adam and Eve. But it's not because he doesn't know where they are. The couple is afraid when they hear the "sound" of the Lord (Gen 3:8) because it signals that God is coming in judgment (see Psalm 29:1–9). So instead of seeking his presence and his mercy, they hide themselves.

The Lord puts four questions to Adam and Eve in Genesis 3:9–13: (1) "Where are you?" (2) "Who told you that you were naked?" (3) "Have you eaten of the tree of which I commanded you not to eat?" and (4) "What is this that you have done?"

The Lord, almighty and omniscient, already knows the answers to these questions. But he asks because he wants Adam and Eve to take responsibility for their actions and seek his forgiveness. God, in other words, gives them an opportunity for confession and reconciliation. Nevertheless, instead of owning up to their sin, the couple makes excuses for their disobedience, even pointing a finger of blame at God (Gen 3:12–13).

God turns first to the serpent, who is the instigator of all the trouble. He pronounces upon the serpent a *curse* of humiliation (Gen 3:14), and then he promises a *conqueror*—a future seed of the woman—who will bring about his demise after ages of enmity rage between the offspring of the serpent and that of the woman (Gen 3:15).

God turns next to the couple to spell out the consequences of their sin. Pain will

accompany childbirth, sin will place a strain on the marital relationship, and frustration will hound all human labor, especially the effort to grow food. Indeed, the ground itself will languish under a curse. Finally, physical death will come to all (Gen 3:16–19).

Notice, however, that Adam and Eve undergo a spiritual death in the garden, not a physical death. On the day they eat the forbidden fruit, they drive the divine life of God out of their souls. They incur spiritual death, which is a tragedy far more dreadful than physical death. The original sin of Adam and Eve is the first mortal sin, which the Church defines as a "death of the soul" (CCC 403).

Immediately Adam and Eve experience loss. Their innocence and intimacy with the Lord are lost; the harmony they enjoyed with each other and with creation is also lost. The serpent seduced them into trying to be like God but without obedience to God. As a result, they plunged both themselves and their descendants into spiritual slavery and death (CCC 398).

Still, the Lord is merciful to Adam and Eve. He covers their nakedness with animal skins, suggesting that sacrifices had been made to cover their shame. And then he expels them from the garden, posting cherubim (i.e. angels) at its entrance, lest the man and woman seal their damnation by eating from the Tree of Life (Gen 3:21–22).

The First Gospel

Far from giving up on his fallen children, however, God promises a coming Savior—one who will vanquish the serpent and set matters right once again (Gen 3:15). The Fathers of the Church referred to this promise as the *protoevangelium*, a Latin term meaning "first announcement of the gospel" (CCC 410). They even saw an allusion to the Virgin Birth of the Savior in the expression "seed of the woman" insofar

as "seed" (*sperma* in Greek) normally comes from a man and not a woman.

The promise of a Savior is a promise of a "new Adam" and a "new Eve" who will redeem the human race by undoing the damage caused by the first Adam and Eve (CCC 410–411). The new Adam will triumph over the serpent, and the new Eve will be his mother. Just as the first Adam and Eve brought death into the world, so the new Adam and Eve—Jesus and his mother Mary—will restore eternal life to the world (see Rom 5:12–21; 1 Cor 15:21–22, 45–49).

In the garden, Adam feared natural death more than spiritual death, only to draw upon himself *both* kinds of death. In contrast, Jesus accepts suffering and natural death, so that through the cross, he can destroy the devil, who has the power of death, and deliver us from our bondage to sin and fear of death (see Heb 2:14–15).

Jesus comes as a new Adam to bear the curses triggered by the first Adam. He faces his test in a garden as Adam did (Gethsemane, Matt 26:36–46); the sweat of his brow, signifying Adam's burden after the Fall, becomes like drops of blood (Luke 22:44); the thorns that sprouted from the ground following Adam's sin are woven around his head as a crown (Matt 27:29); and he is stripped naked to suffer the primordial shame of Adam and Eve (Matt 27:28, 31, 35). His death on a tree is also significant, since the cross was called the "Tree of Life" in the ancient Church. Finally, it is when Jesus enters the sleep of death that his Bride—the Church—is fashioned from his pierced side (see John 19:34).

In all of this, Jesus offers his life as the perfect sacrifice of love. Unlike the first

Adam, the new Adam yields his will entirely to the Father's will and trusts him completely. He lays down his life out of love for his Bride, the Church, and he restores to her what was lost through the sin of the first Adam. Even more remarkable, Jesus gives us a share in his own divine life, so that we can become partakers of the divine nature.

Catholic tradition, working from the premise that Jesus is the new Adam, has long seen Mary as "the new Eve." Here again the new is a mirror image of the old: Eve was deceived and transgressed God's commandment, but Mary gives herself to God in total obedience: "Behold, I am the handmaid of the Lord; let it be to me according to your word" (Luke 1:38).

The story of Scripture is a love story. It is the revelation of God's love for the world. The sign of that love in the beginning is the marriage of Adam and Eve. The union of the first couple, though beautiful, points beyond itself to something even more wonderful: the truth that God desires a "nuptial" or "marital" union with humanity, a covenant bond between lovers that lasts forever!

God wants nothing more than to give himself to his people, and for his people to give themselves to him. The love demanded by the covenant is total. It is a life-giving love that images the inner life of the Trinity. You and I must learn to love as the Trinity loves, because our destiny — the thing for which we are made — is to share in the eternal divine love that unites Father, Son, and Spirit. Ultimately it is from God himself that we learn how to pour out our lives for others.

Scripture tells the story of God raising his children from infancy to maturity. Little by little he teaches us, guides us, disciplines us, and woos us back into his arms. Through this whole process he is making us ready for the wedding supper of the Lamb, the eternal feast of his love in heaven. One would be hard-pressed to find a better sign of the tender union that God desires with us than the most intimate of human relationships. Yet this is why we exist — to live in the Lord's embrace forever!

✪What We'll Cover in Lesson 5

Themes Covered

❖ Cain's sin

❖ The deluge and a new creation

❖ The Tower of Babel

❖ The righteous and wicked generations

Scripture Verses Read in Lesson 5

❖ Genesis 6:18

❖ Genesis 8:20–22

❖ 1 Peter 3:20–21

Notes

Adam + Eve

Cain   Abel. - killed by Cain.   Seth

Seth

Review Questions

1. According to Genesis, the descendants of both Cain and Ham commit the same sin. What is it?

_____

_____

_____

_____

2. What are some of the parallels between the Creation account and the story of the Flood?

_____

_____

_____

_____

3. Explain how baptism is prefigured by the biblical Flood.

_____

_____

_____

_____

Discussion Questions

1. Can you think of anything in this lesson that you've never considered before, or even heard before? If so, how might this new information impact your relationship with God and others?

_____

_____

_____

_____

2. Do you see any parallels between the sins of Cain, Ham, and their descendants, and the sins of our modern culture? Explain.

_____

_____

_____

_____

3. God sent judgment on the builders of Babel by confusing their language. What are some ways that miscommunication causes problems in the modern world?

_____

_____

_____

_____

This Lesson's Memory Verse

"[W]hen God's patience waited in the days of Noah, during the building of the ark, in which a few, that is, eight persons, were saved through water. Baptism, which corresponds to this, now saves you, not as a removal of dirt from the body but as an appeal to God for a clear conscience, through the resurrection of Jesus Christ."

1 PETER 3:20–21

Preparation for the Next Lesson

❖ *A Father Who Keeps His Promises* by Dr. Scott Hahn, chs. 5 & 6

❖ Genesis 12, 15, 17, 22

OUR FATHER IN FAITH

Review of the Previous Lesson

Cain's Sin

Last time we looked at the covenant with Adam and Eve. Their violation of this covenant—the first sin—set their descendants on a path toward greater and greater wickedness. And yet God did not abandon them. Rather, the Lord promised redemption through a coming Savior—a messianic seed, through whom God's covenant purposes would at last be fulfilled (Gen 3:15).

This same promise announces that human history will be marked by an ongoing conflict between two seeds, the seed of the woman (the *righteous* of the world) and the seed of the serpent (the *wicked* of the world). This longstanding "enmity" announced in Genesis 3:15 makes its debut in the story of Cain and Abel, one generation after Adam and Eve.

The setting for this story is a double offering of sacrifice. Cain and Abel both make an offering to the Lord. But although God is pleased with Abel's gift, he is displeased with Cain's, and this makes Cain very angry. Aware of this, God comes to Cain and urges him to fight the temptation that is seeking to master him. But to no avail. Cain is overcome by envy, and he slays his brother Abel in cold blood (Gen 4:7–8).

When God confronts Cain, he gives him an opportunity for repentance, just as he'd done for Adam and Eve after their sin. But just like his parents, Cain churns out excuses rather than making a good confession. He even insinuates that God is unduly harsh in his exercise of justice (Gen 4:13–14).

After Adam and Eve sinned, God cursed the serpent but not the ground. Cain, however, is "cursed from the ground" by God (Gen 4:11) and departs from Eden to wander as a fugitive in a land called Nod (Gen 4:16). Even now, the Lord in his mercy puts a mark of protection on Cain lest he should be slain for murdering his brother (Gen 4:15).

We must understand that the curses of the covenant are not mean-spirited acts of God. Curses are more accurately viewed as fatherly chastisements that are meant to help sinners break free from their sins. God doesn't punish sinners because he stops loving them. Just the opposite. God sends his punishments on sinners because he can't stop loving them!

Adam's Family Divided

Following the banishment and death of Cain and Abel, respectively, Adam and Eve bring another son into the world named Seth. He becomes the father of a righteous family line. This sets the stage for conflict between the lines of Seth and Cain, the two sons (i.e. seeds) of Adam and Eve.

Cain and the Wicked Line. According to Genesis, Cain fathers a son named Enoch, and then he builds a city and names it after Enoch. This implies that Cain is intent upon glorifying himself. Then, by the time we reach the seventh generation from Adam, we see evil continue to sprout and grow in Cain's line. Lamech, one of Cain's descendants, is a bigamist. Contrary to God's plan for marriage established at creation, he takes two wives. Beyond this, he is vindictive and violent (Gen 4:19, 23–24).

Seth and the Righteous Line. Unlike Cain and his descendants, Seth and his descendants foster a prayerful relationship with God. They call upon the "name" (Hebrew, *shem*) of the Lord in worship (Gen 4:26). In other words, they seek to glorify God's name rather than their own. And again, by the time we reach the seventh generation from Adam, we see righteousness burst into bloom in the person of Enoch, who walks closely with the Lord, so much so that God took him (Gen 5:24) so that "he should not see death" (Heb 11:5).

Unfortunately, these parallel lines begin to merge in Genesis 6, when the godly line of Seth intermarries with the ungodly line of Cain. The men of Seth's line, called the "sons of God," are enamored by the beautiful women of Cain's line, called the "daughters of men," and they take them to be their wives (Gen 6:2). The result: the offspring of these unions turn out to be mighty warriors called "the men of renown" (Gen 6:4). In Hebrew, they are literally "the men of the name (*shem*)." Here again the word *shem* refers to the glory and reputation that these men seek for themselves, instead of seeking God's glory. We are not surprised to learn, then, that wickedness sweeps over the earth once the righteous line of Seth mingles itself with the godless line of Cain (Gen 6:5).

Saved through Water

You might say the intermarriage of the Sethites and the Cainites is the straw that breaks the camel's back. Once this happens, the whole earth becomes corrupt—except for Noah, who alone "walked with God" (Gen 6:9). Judgment on humanity's wickedness must be poured out. And yet, because Noah and his family are a righteous remnant, God will intervene to save them. Through them he will bring about a new beginning for the world.

So the Lord instructs Noah to build an ark that will save his family, along with every species of beast and bird, from the flood that is coming. Acting on faith (Heb 11:7), Noah obeyed and did all that God commanded him (Gen 6:22). He thus stands as a witness to the just judgment of God (the Flood) as well as his mercy (the ark). Even more, God will renew his original covenant with creation through Noah and his household (Gen 6:18).

This connection between Creation and the Flood is suggested by parallels between Genesis 1–2 and Genesis 6–8. In both stories, a new world emerges from the engulfing waters of the "deep" (Gen 1:2; 7:11). Likewise, the number seven features prominently in both accounts: as the world was created in seven days, so Noah brings *seven* pairs of "clean animals" (i.e. animals suitable for sacrifice) aboard the ark (Gen 7:2); he waits *seven* days inside the ark before the floodwaters come (Gen 7:10); the ark touches down in the *seventh* month after the floodwaters recede (Gen 8:4); Noah sends birds in search of land every *seven* days (Gen 8:10–12); and Noah's name in Hebrew means "rest" or "relief" (Gen 5:29), calling to mind the *seventh* day of rest (Gen 2:1–4). If the sign of God's covenant with creation is the Sabbath, the sign of God's renewed covenant with creation is the rainbow (Gen 9:12–13).

In the last lesson, we saw God making a covenant with Adam as a *husband*. In this lesson, we see God renewing his covenant with Noah, who's the *father of a household*. It is with Noah and his family—four married couples in all—that God renews his covenant with creation. Noah is thus cast in the role of a new Adam. He is established as the new head of humanity and the mediator through whom God is "re-founding" his covenant family.

Parallels between Adam and Noah help us to see this in Genesis. Both Adam and Noah are told to be "fruitful and multiply, and fill the earth" (Gen 1:28; 9:1). Both are given royal authority over the world of animals (Gen 1:28; 9:2). Both have their nakedness exposed after consuming fruit (Gen 3:6–7; 9:21) in a garden or vineyard (Gen 2:15; 9:20). Finally, just as Adam's descendants split into righteous and wicked lines, so Noah's descendants will do as well.

The Table of Nations

Genesis 10 traces the genealogy of Noah from the patriarch and his sons to the seventy nations that spring from them. This is known as "the table of nations," and it's unique among ancient genealogies in portraying the human race as a single family with a common origin. Just as the human family had its beginning in Adam, so its new beginning is embodied in Noah. With the table of nations in hand, the people of God could find their place in the world.

But the same pattern we observed before the Flood repeats itself after. The descendants of Noah's firstborn son, Shem, emerge as a righteous line that seeks God's glory, and the descendants

In time, sin gains mastery over the descendants of Noah, just as it had over the descendants of Adam. Matters come to a head at the Tower of Babel in Genesis 11, where humanity draws the judgment of God upon itself again. In fact, there is reason to think that the builders of this tower are descendants of Ham—those who stand apart from the line of *Shem* and seek instead to make a shem ("name") for themselves (Gen 11:4). Notice how the Babel story is sandwiched between two genealogies of Shem, one in Gen 10:21–32, and another in Gen 11:10–30.

The *Catechism* states that fallen humanity, firmly in the grip of paganism, is "united only in its perverse ambition to forge its own unity as at Babel" (CCC 57). As a result, the Lord intervenes again with his judgment. The rebels are confused in their language and scattered over the earth.

In the end, God's covenant with Noah, being a renewal of the covenant with creation, is all-embracing. It's established between God and Noah and "all flesh that is upon the earth" (Gen 9:17). Even today this covenant remains in force until the gospel is proclaimed to all the world (CCC 58).

Remember too that the covenant with Noah, made in the aftermath of the Flood, points in a prophetic way to the Sacrament of Baptism. In other words, the Flood is a type of baptism, which cleanses and destroys sin. Just as a renewed creation emerges from the waters, so also those who are baptized come forth as new creations in Christ (see 1 Pet 3:20–21).

of Noah's younger son, Ham, run after vainglory. In fact, as we have seen, the very name *Shem*, which in Hebrew translates to "name," is used in the early chapters of Genesis to mean "fame" or "glory."

The Israelites trace their origin back to Shem, who is the father of the "Shemites." Likewise, within the blessed line of Shem stands a figure named Eber, who is the father the "Hebrews." Eber's children are the ancestors of the Genesis patriarchs: Abraham, Isaac, and Jacob (Gen 11:10–26).

Ham's line, however, is marred by conflict and corruption. The list of his descendants is practically a Who's Who roster of Israel's historical foes. From Ham, the son of Noah, comes the Egyptians, the Canaanites, the Philistines, the Assyrians, and the Babylonians—all peoples who caused great suffering to the nation of Israel in the Old Testament (Gen 10:6–20).

Literary Framework of Genesis 1–11

To modern readers, the genealogies of Genesis can seem unimportant. But understanding how they work helps to reveal the message and artistry of the book. The stories in Genesis are structured and linked together by references to "generations" (in Hebrew, *toledoth* [toe-leh-dóth]). This expression first appears in Genesis 2:4, which speaks of "the generations of the heavens and the earth," and from there it moves the story forward through the lines of Adam (Gen 5:1) and Noah (Gen 6:9).

Repeated references to *generations* show us the literary framework of Genesis. The term occurs another *ten times* in the book (after Gen 2:4) to introduce key figures in the unfolding story. It draws us into the plot of the book and the unfolding of God's plan in history. History, then, is more than politics, economics, and war; it's mainly about the covenant family that God is gathering together in the midst of a fallen world.

Through genealogies, Genesis links Adam and Eve to the rest of salvation history, to Noah, Abraham, Isaac, and Jacob. Careful study of them reveals that spiritual conflict shapes the course and direction of salvation history. It shows us that godliness and ungodliness are often intergenerational, traveling down different family lines.

Ten generations span the distance from Adam to Noah (Gen 5:1–32). Godliness appears in the line of Seth, while wickedness is conspicuous in the line of Cain. At the end of the ten generations, God brings judgment in the raging waters of the Flood. Another ten generations span the distance from Shem, Noah's firstborn son, to Terah, the father of Abram (whose name later becomes Abraham). Again, godliness appears in the line of Shem, while wickedness is conspicuous in the line of Ham. At the end of the second stretch of ten generations, God brings judgment at the Tower of Babel.

We have seen in the last two lessons that humanity after the Fall is beset by conflict. There is a struggle between two *seeds* (Gen 3:15), two *sons* (Gen 4:1–16), and two genealogical *lines* (Gen 4:17—5:32). Saint Augustine, in his work *The City of God*, explained this as an antithesis between two cities—the City of God, signifying people who love God, even to the point of having contempt for themselves, and the City of Man, signifying people who love themselves, even to the point of having contempt for God. This presents us with a significant challenge: How can we live *amidst* the City of Man and yet live *as* the City of God?

☻What We'll Cover in Lesson 6

Themes Covered

❖ The faith of Abram

❖ The priest-king Melchizedek

❖ The three promises and three oaths

❖ The obedience of Abraham and Isaac

❖ The pattern of the elder serving the younger

Scripture Verses Read in Lesson 6

❖ Genesis 12:1–3

❖ Hebrews 6:13–17

❖ Hebrews 6:19–7:2

❖ Galatians 3:14–17

Notes

Review Questions

1. The Lord makes three promises to Abram/Abraham in Genesis 12:1–3. What are these promises?

_____

_____

_____

_____

2. Explain how the three promises of Genesis 12:1–3 relate to the oaths that the Lord swears to Abram/Abraham in Genesis 15, 17, and 22.

_____

_____

_____

_____

3. Explain how God the Father's offering of Jesus is prefigured by Abraham's offering of Isaac.

_____

_____

_____

_____

Discussion Questions

1. Can you think of anything in this lesson that you've never considered before, or even heard before? If so, how might this new information impact your relationship with God and others?

_____

_____

_____

_____

2. Abraham shows remarkable obedience when God calls him to leave everything and set out for the land of Canaan. What lessons does his obedience hold for us? Also, imagine how this must have looked to his peers. Discuss what radical Christian obedience might look like in today's world.

_____

_____

_____

_____

3. We learn from the story of Abraham that God always fulfills his promises, but always according to his timing. How has this proven true in your own life?

_____

_____

_____

_____

This Lesson's Memory Verse

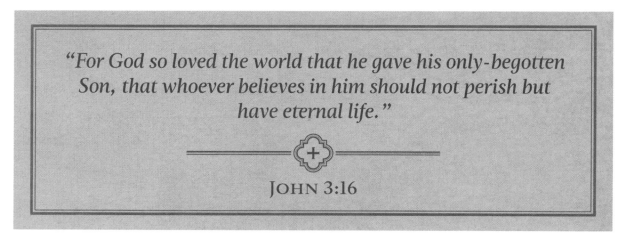

"For God so loved the world that he gave his only-begotten Son, that whoever believes in him should not perish but have eternal life."

✠

JOHN 3:16

Preparation for the Next Lesson

❖ *A Father Who Keeps His Promises* by Dr. Scott Hahn, ch. 7

❖ Exodus 1–3; 4:21–23; 12; 19; 24:1; 25:9

FROM EGYPT TO SINAI

Review of the Previous Lesson

And God Blessed Them . . .

In the beginning, God blessed his creation with the gift of "life." This blessing of the covenant is then transmitted through the family. We see this in Genesis, where blessings are passed down from fathers to sons—from Noah to Shem, for example, through whom the Lord's blessing is channeled to his descendants (see Gen 9:26–27).

But when humanity unites in opposition to God at the Tower of Babel, the blessing that God desires for the world is placed in jeopardy, and the people of the world are scattered and divided. This sets the stage for Abraham: God made a series of promises and covenants with Abraham that included blessing all nations. Ultimately, God will use Abraham and his obedience to bring blessings that undo the curses that were drawn upon the world by Adam and his disobedience.

When God first calls Abram/Abraham in Genesis 12:1–3, he uses the language of bless and *blessing* five times. The blessing that passed from Noah to Shem has now reached Abraham, and through Abraham and his family it will eventually reach the entire world. The human race will not be united by making a name for itself; instead, God will reunite the world by making Abraham's name great.

The scope of God's covenant is again enlarged. The covenant with Adam was made with a *husband and his bride*. The covenant with Noah was made with the *father of a household*. The covenant with Abraham extends even further, since he is the *chieftain of a tribe*.

Abram/Abraham Walks by Faith

Abram/Abraham begins his journey toward blessing by heeding God's call to pull up his tent stakes and move to the Promised Land. But he soon discovers that the road to blessing passes through a forest of trials that include a famine (Gen 12:10), a time of exile (Gen 12:10–20), family strife (Gen 13:2–7), the upheaval of war (Genesis 14:1–16), the disappointment of promises unfulfilled (Gen 15:2), spousal tension (Gen 16:5), painful surgery (Gen 17:24), and the banishment of a dear son (21:8–14). On top of all this, he is asked to take the life of his beloved son by making him a sacrifice to God (Gen 22:1–19).

God's promise to bless Abram is nevertheless fulfilled in Genesis 14:17–20. Having defeated his enemies, he encounters Melchizedek, king of Salem (which eventually becomes Jerusalem). Melchizedek is more than just a king, however; he is a *priest* of God who offers bread and wine to Abram, along with God's blessing. Melchizedek is thus considered a type of Christ, since (1) he is both a priest and a king, (2) his signature offering is bread and wine, and (3) he is given homage.

Three Promises become Covenants

Genesis 12 begins with God making three promises to Abram/Abraham: he will be granted (1) *a land for building a nation*, (2) *a great name or royal dynasty*, and (3) *blessings for the whole world*. Each one of these promises is upgraded to a covenant as the story unfolds in Genesis 15, 17, and 22.

The First Covenant Oath: Genesis 15. In response to Abram's act of faith, in which he believed God's divine promise of a son, God makes a covenant by passing between animals that Abram had cut in two. This time he pledges on oath what he had promised to Abraham at his call: a new homeland on which his descendants can live and grow as a nation (compare Gen 12:1 and Gen 15:12–21).

Nevertheless, Abram and Sarai become impatient as they wait for the Lord to give them a child. So they decide to act on their own. Sarai urges Abram to father a son through her handmaid, Hagar the Egyptian (Gen 16:1–3). Abram consents to the plan, but once Hagar conceives, tension within his household begins to grow (Gen 16:4).

The Second Covenant Oath: Genesis 17. God then decides to intervene by swearing another covenant oath to Abram, whose name he changes to "Abraham." The child born of Hagar will *not* be his heir; rather, Sarai, renamed "Sarah," will herself have a son. In fact, the couple will have countless descendants, and even a royal dynasty—"kings of peoples"—will come from their family line (Gen 17:6). This announcement points forward to the covenant that God will make with David to establish his kingdom in 2 Sam 7:9. It likewise strengthens the promise made to Abraham at his call: God will make his name great with a blessing of royal dignity (Gen 12:2).

One year later, God fulfills his promise as Sarah gives birth to Isaac. Abraham hosts a great feast when the infant is weaned, but Sarah fears that Ishmael will seek Isaac's inheritance, so she presses Abraham to banish the boy and his mother from the camp (Gen 21:10). Abraham enacts her wish, but only after he is nudged by the Lord (Gen 21:12).

The Third Covenant Oath: Genesis 22. Following the expulsion of Ishmael, Abraham is left with his beloved son Isaac and no other sons. The stage is set for the ultimate test: the Lord will instruct Abraham to sacrifice Isaac on a mountain in the land of Moriah (Gen 22:1–2). Despite the instinct to refuse, Abraham promptly takes Isaac, journeys for three days to the designated place, and his son carries the wood for the altar fire to the mountaintop (Gen 22:3–6). When Isaac inquires, "Where is the lamb for the burnt offering?" his father replies, "God will provide himself the lamb" (Gen 22:7–8).

The story reaches its highpoint when Abraham binds his son and prepares to sacrifice him as the Lord commanded. But just before Isaac is slain, Abraham is told to spare the life of his son. A ram seen nearby will be offered in his place. Immediately, for the third and last time, God swears an oath to Abraham, this time pledging to bless all the nations of the world through his seed (Gen 22:11–18).

God's promise in Genesis 3:15 to crush the head of the serpent through the "seed" of the woman is now specified further: this coming Savior will be the "seed" of Abraham. And who is this

awaited seed? It is Jesus Christ, the "son of Abraham" (Matt 1:1).

The human race languishes under the curse triggered by Adam's disobedience. Now God is pledging to restore his blessing to humanity in response to Abraham's obedience—offering his beloved son as a sacrifice. In the third divine oath sworn to Abraham, God's solution to the problem of sin and death is revealed: through Abraham's "seed"—the Messiah—the ancient curse will be lifted at last.

Three Covenant Oaths

The three covenants that God makes with Abraham give us an outline of the rest of salvation history. Genesis 15, which foretells that Abram's descendants will receive the Promised Land after a time of enslavement, is fulfilled in the Exodus and *Mosaic covenant*. Genesis 17, which foresees a dynasty of kings among the descendants of Abraham and Sarah, is fulfilled in the kingdom established by the *Davidic covenant*. And Genesis 22, which prophesies blessing for all nations through Abraham's seed, is fulfilled in Jesus Christ and the *New covenant*.

The Obedience of Abraham and Isaac

Abraham is not the only person who acts as God commands. Isaac, the biblical account implies, was also obedient. Rabbinic tradition calls this story the *Aqedah*, a term that refers to the "binding" of Isaac (see Gen 22:9). We often envision Isaac as a purely passive figure in this drama, but in fact he was old enough and strong enough to carry the firewood up the mountain. Clearly, he could have resisted his father, now more than 100 years old, if he had not agreed to be tied down for the sacrifice. There is even a Jewish tradition that Isaac asked to be bound, lest he should fail to obey God's command.

The Fathers of the Church saw the sacrifice of Christ foreshadowed in this story. Jesus, like Isaac of old, is the beloved Son of his Father (John 3:16); he carries the wood of his sacrifice up a mountain (John 19:17); his Father does not spare him, even in the face of death (Rom 8:32); and he rises to new life on the third day, recalling how Abraham received his son back alive at the end of the three-day ordeal (1 Cor 15:4). And, according to the Book of Hebrews, Abraham had a resurrection faith: he "considered that God was able to raise men even from the dead" (Heb 11:6).

The liturgy of the Church also reads Genesis in connection with the Transfiguration, when the Father reveals the identity of Jesus to the apostles, saying: "This is my beloved Son" (Mark 9:7). These words echo the description of Isaac in God's command to Abraham: "Take your son,

your only-begotten son Isaac, whom you love, and go to the land of Moriah, and offer him there as a burnt offering upon one of the mountains of which I shall tell you" (Genesis 22:2).

In the end, while Isaac was *nearly* sacrificed, Jesus was *actually* sacrificed. Why? Because this was the Father's plan for bringing all the covenants of salvation history to fulfillment. The sacrifice of the beloved Son is the way in which God's blessings will pour out for all nations. Abraham's prophecy, that "God will provide himself the lamb" (Gen 22:8), finally comes true in Jesus. Even the place where Abraham took Isaac, Mount Moriah, is the elevation in Jerusalem where Solomon built the Temple (2 Chron 3:1).

A Scriptural Pattern: The Elder Serves the Younger

A subplot is noticeable in Scripture in which younger siblings are preferred to older siblings. Recall that God had chosen

Isaac over his older brother Ishmael, and later he chooses Jacob over his older brother Esau. In the next generation, the Lord favors Joseph to his older brothers, who sell him into slavery. The idea is that God selects the weaker and younger to show that it's *his divine power*, not man's power, that accomplishes his plan.

Saint Paul touches on this in the New Testament when he clarifies that God chooses the younger over the older "in order that God's purpose of election might continue, not because of works because of his call . . . So it depends not upon man's will or exertion, but upon God's mercy" (Rom 9:11, 16).

Into Egypt

Just as "Abraham" is the new name God gave to Abram, so "Israel" is the new name God gave to Jacob. The twelves tribes of Israel are descended from the twelve sons of the patriarch Jacob/Israel. One of those sons, Joseph, is betrayed by his brothers and taken as a slave to Egypt, where he is blessed by God and elevated to a high position in the Egyptian government. Eventually a famine brings Joseph's brothers down to Egypt in search of food, and once Joseph reveals himself to them, the family of Jacob/Israel is reunited and given a place to live and thrive in Egypt—thrive, that is, until a new Pharaoh rises who enslaves the people of Israel. God's promise to Abraham begins to take shape: "your descendants will be sojourners in a land that is not theirs and will be slaves there . . . but I will bring judgment on the nation which they serve, and afterward they shall come out with great possessions" (Genesis 15:13–14).

✪What We'll Cover in Lesson 7

Themes Covered

- ❖ The firstborn sonship of Israel
- ❖ The slavery of Israel in Egypt
- ❖ The call of Moses
- ❖ The first Passover and deliverance of Israel
- ❖ The covenant with Israel at Sinai

Scripture Verses Read in Lesson 7

- ❖ Exodus 2:23–25
- ❖ Exodus 2:11–16
- ❖ Exodus 3:1–8
- ❖ Ezekiel 20:6–9
- ❖ 1 Corinthians 10:1–6
- ❖ Exodus 24:3–8
- ❖ Exodus 24:9–11
- ❖ Hebrews 8:5
- ❖ Isaiah 6:1–3

Notes

Review Questions

1. In the Book of Exodus, God brings judgment on the gods of the Egyptians. How does this happen?

_____

_____

_____

_____

2. What, according to the study, was the main purpose of the Exodus?

_____

_____

_____

_____

3. What is the significance of the Israelites bowing in worship before the Egyptian god Apis?

_____

_____

_____

_____

Discussion Questions

1. Can you think of anything in this lesson that you've never considered before, or even heard before? If so, how might this new information impact your relationship with God and others?

_____

_____

_____

_____

2. Moses encountered the living God, manifest in glory, at the burning bush. Have you ever felt the presence of the Lord in a palpable way? In what ways did it change you or the direction of your life?

_____

_____

_____

_____

3. Take a look at the conversation between God and Moses in Exodus 3:13–4:17. What are some excuses that we make for resisting God's calling for our life?

_____

_____

_____

_____

This Lesson's Memory Verse

> *"Moses came and told the people all the words of the LORD and all the ordinances; and all the people answered with one voice, and said, 'All the words which the LORD has spoken we will do.'"*
>
>
>
> EXODUS 24:3

Preparation for the Next Lesson

❖ *A Father Who Keeps His Promises* by Dr. Scott Hahn, chs. 8 & 9

❖ Exodus 32

❖ Ezekiel 20:1–26

WANDERING IN THE WILDERNESS

Review of the Previous Lesson

God's Firstborn Son

Salvation history is the story of God gathering a family to himself. At creation, he fashions Adam as his firstborn son, and yet Adam proves to be unfaithful. Still, the Lord does not give up on us. Instead he pledges to restore his blessings to men and women through the seed of Abraham.

In Genesis we see that families grow and become nations. Israel, the nation that looks to Abraham as a great-grandfather, is designated God's "firstborn" among the nations (Exod 4:22). But following in the footsteps of Adam, Israel falls short of its calling and proves to be another unfaithful firstborn son. Even so, it's not all gloom and doom. Like any good father, God bends down to the level of his wayward children with the aim of raising them up again.

The Book of Exodus tells how God acts to fulfill his covenant with Abraham—specifically, his pledge to deliver his offspring and give them a new homeland (see Gen 15:13–18). But we should recognize that God has a larger purpose in mind than liberating Abraham's descendants from political bondage. More than anything, he wants to rescue them from *spiritual* bondage. Scripture informs us that God's people, while living for centuries in Egypt, had attached themselves to the gods of Egypt (Ezek 20:6–9). Thus, the primary purpose of the Exodus is to bring the Israelites out of Egypt, so they can break free from idolatry and worship the Lord, the only true God. "Let my people go, that they may serve me in the wilderness" is Moses' message from God to Pharaoh (Exod 7:16).

The Call of Moses

The story begins with a decree of slavery and death. Afraid that the population of Hebrew slaves was growing too large, Pharaoh orders the enslavement of the Israelites (Exod 1:8–11) and the drowning of every newborn boy among them (Exod

1:22). One of these infants is saved when his mother places him in a basket on the Nile. Providentially, the Pharaoh's daughter finds the child and raises him in the royal court. Because the boy was "taken from the water," she names him "Moses" (Exod 2:10).

Fast forward forty years. Moses, now a grown man, sees a fellow Hebrew being beaten by an Egyptian taskmaster. Filled with indignation, he intervenes, kills the Egyptian, and is forced to flee the country. For the next forty years he lives with a family of Midianites as a shepherd (Exod 2:11–22).

One day, while tending his flock near Mount Sinai, he sees a bush that is on fire but is not consumed. From the midst of it, the Lord, the God of Abraham, Isaac, and Jacob, speaks to Moses and announces his plan to save his people from slavery in Egypt and bring them to the Promised Land (Exod 3:6–8). Moses is told to return to Egypt, to seek an audience with Pharaoh, and to request that Israel be granted a three-day leave to offer sacrifices to the Lord in the wilderness. He is also informed that Pharaoh will refuse, and his refusal will lead to God's judgment and the release of God's people.

Deliverance from Egypt

But why must Israel's worship take place out in the wilderness? Because the Egyptians will find their sacrifices an "abomination"—a form of sacrilege that will instigate violence (Exod 8:26). Implied in this prospect is an unstated fact: many of the gods of Egypt were represented as animals. Sacrificing animals in the service of another god will hardly sit well with the Egyptians. But this is precisely what the Lord is calling for. He wants his people to *renounce* the idol gods of Egypt and *return* to him as the only true God.

Pharaoh refuses to grant the Israelites time off, and as a result, God brings ten devastating plagues on Egypt. These calamities affect the people, land, and livestock of Egypt, but they also symbolize God's judgment on the gods of Egypt (Num 33:4). The first nine plagues caused great suffering but not a softening of Pharaoh's hardened heart. So the Lord threatened one more plague: the death of every firstborn in the land (Exod 11:4–9). The Israelites, however, are given a means to save their firstborn sons: the celebration of Passover (Exod 12:1–27).

The rite of Passover requires every household to *sacrifice* an unblemished lamb, to *smear* its blood on the doorframes of their homes, and to *eat* the lamb in the course of a sacred meal. The final plague "passed over" every house that observed these commands, sparing their firstborns (Exod 12:13).

Pharaoh's will is finally broken when his firstborn dies in the tenth plague, and Israel is released from bondage (Exod 12:30–32). The people flee the country that night, led by the Lord in a pillar of cloud and fire (Exod 13:21). The journey takes them through the parted waters of the sea (Exod 14:21–22), and when they complain of being hungry and thirsty, the Lord provides bread from heaven and water from a rock (Exod 16–17).

According to Saint Paul, all of this prefigures our salvation through the Sacraments. As the Lord led Israel to freedom through the sea, so we are saved through baptism into Christ and the leading of the Holy Spirit. And as the Israelites were fed by miracles of bread and water, so we are nourished with the spiritual food and drink of the Eucharist (1 Cor 10:1–4).

The First Covenant with Israel

The journey reaches a climax when the people arrive at Mount Sinai. There the Lord seals a covenant with Israel. He gives his people the Ten Commandments (Exod 20:1–17) and a short collection of civil laws (Exod 21–23). If the children of Israel will keep God's covenant, they will fulfill their mission to be "a kingdom of priests and a holy nation" (Exod 19:6).

Moses prepares for the covenant ceremony by building an altar of sacrifice and setting up twelve stone pillars to symbolize Israel's twelve tribes. The ceremony begins with animal sacrifices, continues with Moses splashing "the blood of the covenant" on the people, and is fully ratified when Moses and the elders of Israel ascend Mount Sinai and share a sacred meal in the presence of God (Exod 24:5–11).

After the covenant at Sinai is sealed, Moses climbs up the mountain again and sees "the pattern of the tabernacle" (Exod 25:9). It's a heavenly image of the earthly sanctuary that God wishes to pitch in the midst of his people. What Moses sees, in other words, is the Lord's temple in heaven. The prophets of Israel caught glimpses of this celestial dwelling, but its fullest description is given in the Book of Revelation (Rev 21–22).

❂What We'll Cover in Lesson 8

Themes Covered

❖ The golden calf incident

❖ The second covenant with Israel

❖ The change in the priesthood and the laws of Deuteronomy

❖ The Ark of the Covenant

❖ The "New Moses" and "New Passover"

Scripture Verses Read in Lesson 8

❖ Exodus 32:7–10

❖ Galatians 3:19

❖ Matthew 19:8

❖ 1 Corinthians 5:6–8

❖ Matthew 26:26–28

Notes

Review Questions

1. What was God's original purpose in asking Israel to sacrifice animals? Why, following the events in Exodus 32, does he command the continual sacrifice of animals?

_____

_____

_____

_____

2. In what ways are the person and work of Christ prefigured in Moses?

_____

_____

_____

_____

3. The Eucharist is the new Passover. What are some of the parallels that reveal this?

_____

_____

_____

_____

Discussion Questions

1. Can you think of anything in this lesson that you've never considered before, or even heard before? If so, how might this new information impact your relationship with God and others?

_____

_____

_____

_____

2. Give a few examples of how the people of Israel showed a lack of trust in God. What are some ways that we withhold our trust in the Lord?

_____

_____

_____

_____

3. Scripture shows us that God mercifully accommodates himself and his laws to our failings. What are some ways that God does this with us?

_____

_____

_____

_____

This Lesson's Memory Verse

"Cleanse out the old leaven that you may be new dough, as you really are unleavened. For Christ, our Paschal Lamb, has been sacrificed. Let us, therefore, celebrate the festival, not with the old leaven, the leaven of malice and evil, but with the unleavened bread of sincerity and truth."

1 CORINTHIANS 5:7–8

Preparation for the Next Lesson

❖ *A Father Who Keeps His Promises* by Dr. Scott Hahn, ch. 10

❖ 2 Samuel 6 & 7

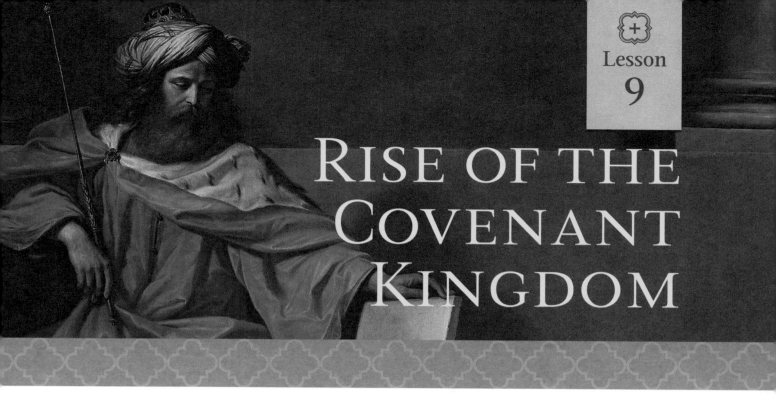

RISE OF THE COVENANT KINGDOM

Review of the Previous Lesson

God's Second Covenant with Israel

At the same time Moses is enveloped in the Lord's presence on Mount Sinai, the Israelites at the foot of the mountain are in rebellion. The nation newly rescued from Egypt is quickly reverting to idolatry. The object of their worship: an image of Apis, the Egyptian bull god (Exod 32:1–6). As it turns out, taking Israel out of Egypt would prove to be easier than taking Egypt out of Israel!

Worship of the calf hints that Israel succumbs to the three temptations of money, sex, and power. (1) The gold of the calf points to the worship of *wealth*; (2) the revelry (i.e. orgies) surrounding the calf signifies surrender to *sexual pleasure*; and (3) the image of a bull calf, which is a Near Eastern symbol of virility, suggests the worship of earthly *strength*.

Having broken the covenant, Israel deserves the curse of the covenant—death. The Lord thus urges Moses: "Let me alone, that my wrath may burn hot against them and I may consume them" (Exod 32:10). But Moses refuses to stand aside and watch his people perish. Instead, he reminds God of the oath he swore to Abraham, Isaac, and Jacob. If Israel is destroyed, the chosen descendants of Abraham will be destroyed. And if that happens, the Lord will default on his promise to bless them and all the nations through them (Exod 32:13).

But the Lord has not forgotten his oath to the patriarchs. On the contrary, he is opening Moses's eyes to see *why* he swore an oath in the first place: God knew long ago that Israel would need it. The Abrahamic covenant was a merciful provision for such a time as this.

Moses then descends the mountain. No sooner does he witness Israel's wickedness than he smashes the tablets inscribed with the Ten Commandments, symbolizing what the Israelites have done—they have broken their covenant with God. Then Moses, filled with righteous anger, shouts: "Who is on the Lord's side?" Only men from the tribe of Levi respond, and being urged to slay the idolaters in the camp, they fell 3,000 sinners that day. Rewarding their zeal, Moses declares of the Levites: "Today you have ordained yourselves for the service of the Lord, each one at the cost of his son and of his brother, that he may bestow a blessing upon you this day" (Exod 32:29).

At this point the law of the covenant changes. Israel has shown itself still enslaved to idols, and so an elaborate code of legal amendments is called for that is suited to Israel's spiritual condition. New laws are given for sacrifice, purity, and morality—mainly in the Book of Leviticus—that are designed to separate Israel from the Gentiles and their pagan practices. Israel must learn the rudiments of holiness before it can fulfill its mission to evangelize the world.

Sacrifice is now mandated as a continual obligation. Israel must renounce the animal gods of Egypt in an ongoing way by the regular offering of cattle, sheep, and goats. There is also a fundamental change in the priesthood. Prior to the golden calf, the whole nation of Israel was to be a "kingdom of priests" (Exod 19:6). Afterwards, ordination is reserved for the Levites alone, specifically for the descendants of Aaron.

Rebellions and Rules

Unfortunately, new laws didn't translate into renewed obedience. Israel's rebellion in the wilderness continues. In fact, the Book of Numbers shows us a pattern in which more laws are given each time Israel commits serious sin. By slowly adding to the weight of the Mosaic law, the Lord hopes to teach his people about their weakness and need for his grace (Gal 3:19).

When, at long last, the pilgrims of Israel reach the border of the Promised Land, they rebel yet again by refusing to enter. They fear to confront the mighty Canaanites in battle, despite God's promise of victory over them (Num 13:30—14:10). The Israelites thus prove themselves beyond rehabilitation. Now the Lord's judgment is severe: not a single person who came out of Egypt—except Joshua and Caleb—will step foot in the Promised Land. Their children will inherit the land; but the parents are sentenced to die in the wilderness (Num 14:20–35).

Nevertheless, even the children prove unfaithful. Even they fall headlong into idolatry (Num 25:1–5), just as their parents did at Mount Sinai (Exod 32:1–6). The result of this second apostasy is the

giving of a "second law"—which is what the word *Deuteronomy* means. In view of his people's sinfulness, God gives them not just additional laws this time but a "lower law." In fact, Deuteronomy makes several concessions to the weaknesses of Israel, permitting such things as divorce and genocidal warfare, which were not included in earlier legislation. Jesus explains that Moses permitted legal concessions such as divorce to cope with Israel's hardness of heart (Matt 19:8).

The early Church Fathers called this an example of "divine condescension." This refers to God, acting as a wise Father, bending down to the level of his children and their needs. In a sense, the law of Deuteronomy lowers the standards of the law to help Israel "grow up." These laws of

Deuteronomy will no longer be necessary when Jesus comes as the Messiah.

Jesus as the New Moses

The events of the Exodus, including the role of Moses as a deliverer, foreshadow the person and work of Jesus Christ. Jesus is born under a murderous king who slays Hebrew baby boys, just as Moses was. Jesus undergoes a period of exile in Egypt until the Lord calls him back to his homeland, just as Israel did. Jesus passes through water at his baptism and spends forty days in the wilderness, just as Moses and his people passed through the sea and spent forty years in the wilderness. Jesus teaches the gospel from a mountain, just as Moses relayed God's law to the people at Mount Sinai. Jesus radiated the glory of God on the mount of Transfiguration, much as Moses's face shone with the glory of God at Sinai. Jesus accomplishes a new Passover and a new deliverance (i.e. a new Exodus) from slavery to sin that is modeled on the original Passover and the liberation of Israel from enslavement in Egypt.

These and other parallels reveal that God choreographs the events of the Old Testament to foreshow the mysteries of Christian salvation in the New Testament. The whole story of God rescuing his people from bondage and bringing them into the Promised Land gives us a preview of what he always planned to accomplish in the Messiah—a new Passover sacrifice, a new Passover meal, a new Exodus deliverance, and a heavenly inheritance in a new Promised Land.

What We'll Cover in Lesson 9

Themes Covered

❖ Israel enters the Promised Land

❖ Israel asks for a king

❖ The fall of King Saul

❖ The rise of King David and his role as a priest-king

❖ Jesus as the "New David"

Scripture Verses Read in Lesson 9

❖ 1 Samuel 8:1–9

❖ Deuteronomy 12:10–11

❖ 2 Samuel 7:8–16

❖ 2 Samuel 6:14, 17–19

Notes

Review Questions

1. God chose Israel's first king from the tribe of Benjamin. Why is this significant?

_____

_____

_____

_____

2. Saul quickly lost favor with God. Why did this happen?

_____

_____

_____

_____

3. David combines two offices and roles in himself. What are these two roles, and in what ways does he exercise them?

_____

_____

_____

_____

Discussion Questions

1. Can you think of anything in this lesson that you've never considered before, or even heard before? If so, how might this new information impact your relationship with God and others?

_____

_____

_____

_____

2. What is the lesson to be learned from Saul's two acts of disobedience?

_____

_____

_____

_____

3. What are some of the ways that David honors Saul as the Lord's anointed king? What lessons can we take away from his example?

_____

_____

_____

_____

This Lesson's Memory Verse

"I will raise up your offspring after you, who shall come forth from your body, and I will establish his kingdom. He shall build a house for my name, and I will establish the throne of his kingdom for ever. I will be his father, and he shall be my son."

2 SAMUEL 7:12–14

Preparation for the Next Lesson

❖ *A Father Who Keeps His Promises* by Dr. Scott Hahn, ch. 11

FEATURES OF THE KINGDOM

Review of the Previous Lesson

Into the Promised Land

Following the death of Moses, Joshua leads the people of Israel into Canaan—the land promised to the descendants of Abraham, Isaac, and Jacob (Josh 3–4). He is their commander in a series of battles to seize control of the land (Josh 6–12). Once claimed, the land is parceled out to the twelve tribes of Israel (Josh 13–21).

After Joshua, God's people struggle for many generations to secure total possession of the land, which is still partly controlled by Canaanites. They also face oppression from outside enemies. God therefore raises up *judges*—men and women empowered by him to deliver the tribes from their foes. In the Book of Judges, the storyline is marked by a series of three Ds: (1) One or more tribes falls into *disobedience*. (2) Then the Lord allows Israel to suffer *defeat*. (3) And finally, when the people cry out for help, God brings them *deliverance* through one of the judges. This cycle repeats itself several times in Judges.

Saul, the First King

As the period of the judges draws to a close, Samuel—a prophet, a priest, and the last of the judges—establishes his sons as judges over Israel. But the people insist that it's time for a change in leadership. They clamor for a king because they want to be ruled like other nations (1 Sam 8:1–5). Conceding to their wishes, Samuel anoints Saul as the first king of Israel (1 Sam 10:1). In doing so, God chooses the weak and humble yet again: Saul is a Benjaminite, and the tribe of Benjamin is the least (smallest) of the twelve tribes of Israel (1 Sam 9:21).

But Saul struggles with disobedience to the word of God. As a consequence of his failures, he is first denied a dynasty, and then he loses his throne.

David's Rise to Power

The Lord then sends Samuel to Bethlehem, to the house of Jesse, who has eight sons. There he anoints David, Jesse's youngest,

as the second king of Israel (1 Sam 16:11–13). Here is a man after God's own heart (1 Sam 13:14). In the name of the Lord of hosts, he slays the Philistine warrior, Goliath of Gath, with a stone hurled from a slingshot (1 Sam 17). Soon he becomes a musician in Saul's royal household, without Saul knowing that David is the future king.

Once Saul discovers that David is the Lord's anointed one, he makes several attempts on David's life. David, by contrast, refuses to lay violent hands on Saul, even when he has the opportunity. When Saul and his sons meet their demise in a war with the Philistines, David mourns him and his son Jonathan (2 Sam 1) and gives Saul's crippled grandson, Mephibosheth, a permanent seat as his table (2 Sam 9).

One of David's early accomplishments is the conquest of Zion (i.e. Jerusalem), the last stronghold of the Canaanites in the land of Israel. This is the place where the Lord desires to dwell among his people. David realizes that, having established peace in the land, the prescription of Deuteronomy 12:10–11 has been fulfilled. The time has come to build a house for the Lord, and David himself wants to begin construction right away—but God has other plans (2 Sam 7:1–2).

David as Liturgical Leader

Back at Mount Sinai, Israel received its calling to be a "kingdom of priests" (Exod 19:6). But God's people failed to live up to that high calling. Now, with David established in Jerusalem, the holy mission of Israel is renewed.

How so? David is not only a *king*; he also performs the services of a priest. In 2 Samuel 6:14–19, we see David engaged in priestly activities: he wears a Levitical garment; he brings the Ark of the Covenant into Jerusalem in a liturgical procession; he offers sacrifices before the Lord; and he blesses the people in the name of the Lord.

David is also involved in Israel's worship in other ways. Many of the hymns in the Book of Psalms are attributed to David. The blueprints for the Temple and its services are revealed to David (1 Chron 28:19). The duties of the Levites, musical as well as ministerial, are newly organized by David (1 Chron 15:16–24). Perpetual praise and thanksgiving to the Lord is established by David before the Ark on Mount Zion (1 Chron 16:37–42).

 What We'll Cover in Lesson 10

Themes Covered

❖ The primary and secondary features of the Davidic kingdom

❖ The *todah* or thanksgiving offering

❖ The sin of David

❖ The failures and fall of Solomon and his kingdom

❖ The restoration of the kingdom prophetically foretold

Scripture Verses Read in Lesson 10

❖ Psalm 89:26–27

❖ Psalm 89:19–21

❖ Isaiah 2:1–4

❖ Hebrews 8:5

❖ John 2:19–22

❖ Psalm 50:14–15

❖ Psalm 69:30–31

❖ 2 Samuel 12:1–7, 10–15

❖ Isaiah 9:1–7

❖ Jeremiah 31:31–33

Notes

_____
_____
_____
_____
_____
_____
_____
_____
_____
_____
_____
_____
_____
_____
_____
_____
_____
_____
_____
_____
_____
_____
_____
_____
_____
_____
_____

Review Questions

1. The Davidic covenant has seven major characteristics. What are these characteristics? How do they relate to Jesus Christ and his work?

_____

_____

_____

_____

2. The study speaks about the *todah* offering. What is the *todah*, and how is it celebrated?

_____

_____

_____

_____

3. How would you describe the movement from the Mosaic covenant to the Davidic covenant in terms of their differences?

_____

_____

_____

_____

Discussion Questions

1. Can you think of anything in this lesson that you've never considered before, or even heard before? If so, how might this new information impact your relationship with God and others?

_____

_____

_____

_____

2. What are the circumstances—the near occasions for sin—that paved the way to David's adultery with Bathsheba? What lesson does this hold for us and our avoidance of sin?

_____

_____

_____

_____

3. Scripture describes David as "a man after God's own heart," and yet David commits a series of grave sins. How can both be true? How would you define the expression?

_____

_____

_____

_____

This Lesson's Memory Verse

"Have mercy on me, O God, according to your merciful love; according to your abundant mercy blot out my transgressions. Wash me thoroughly from my iniquity, and cleanse me from my sin! For I know my transgressions, and my sin is ever before me."

PSALM 51:1–3

Preparation for the Next Lesson

❖ *A Father Who Keeps His Promises* by Dr. Scott Hahn, ch. 12

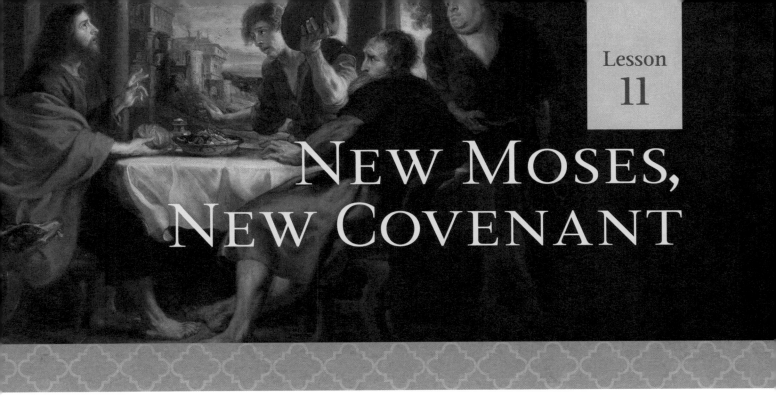

New Moses, New Covenant

Review of the Previous Lesson

Primary Features of the Davidic Covenant

The Davidic covenant is the last in a long line of Old Testament covenants. It represents the high point of God's plan before the coming of Christ. This can be seen in the primary features of the Davidic covenant—that is, in the arrangements that most directly prepare for the New Covenant.

(1) *The Son of David is the Son of God.* The prophet Nathan declares that David's royal son will also be the Lord's son (2 Sam 7:14). For most of David's heirs, this took place when he was anointed as king of Israel. On that day, the day of his coronation, David's son became God's son (Psalm 2:7), his "first-born" (Psalm 89:27). Israel's calling as a royal-priestly firstborn son is partly fulfilled in the Davidic king and ultimately fulfilled in Jesus Christ.

(2) *The Davidic King is a "Messiah."*

Every time a successor of David was anointed, he was known in Hebrew as a *mashiah* [ma-shée-ah] or "anointed one." Ritually, he was anointed with oil, but this merely signified that he was anointed by the Spirit of God (1 Sam 16:13). All the Davidic kings of Israel were anointed, beginning with David and Solomon (1 Kings 1:32–40; 2 Kings 11:12; 23:30; 2 Chron 23:11; Psalm 89:19–21).

Jesus is the anointed king from David's line. In fact, the word "Christ" is simply a Greek term meaning "anointed one." The genealogy of Jesus identifies him as a "son of David" according to his humanity (Matt 1:1), but it's at his baptism that he's anointed by the Holy Spirit (Mark 1:9–11). As soon as Jesus is baptized, he is tempted in the wilderness, and then he returns to Galilee, preaching the kingdom of God.

(3) *The Davidic Kingdom is International.* If the scope of the Mosaic covenant is national, the scope of the Davidic covenant is international. We see this in different ways. David has non-Israelites among his elite fighting forces (1 Chron 11:11–12). Solomon forges treaty covenants between Israel and other nations (1 Kings 5:1–12). The Psalms pray that Solomon's kingdom will extend to the ends of the earth and all nations will come to serve him (Psalm 72:8, 11). This desire is not made a reality until the risen Jesus commissions his followers to make disciples of "all nations" (Matt 28:19) and to carry the gospel "to the end of the earth" (Acts 1:8).

(4) *The Davidic Kingdom is Centered in Jerusalem.* Jerusalem is the political and spiritual capital of the Davidic kingdom. Mount Zion in particular is the height where the nations will gather before the Lord in the time of messianic fulfillment. It is a place that the Most High himself has established (Psalm 87:5). In the New

Testament, Mount Zion is the site of the Last Supper, where Jesus institutes the Eucharist, as well as the place where the first disciples are filled with the Holy Spirit on Pentecost. Ultimately, the mountain in Jerusalem is a sign of the heavenly Mount Zion, the city of the living God (Heb 12:22–24).

(5) *The Temple of Solomon, the House of the Lord.* The Temple built by Solomon in Jerusalem is the place that God chooses for his dwelling (1 Kings 8:27–29). It the designated "place" of Israelite sacrifice that Moses envisioned in Deuteronomy 12:10–12. Beyond this, the Jerusalem Temple is a house of prayer and worship for all nations. In the New Testament, Jesus refers to his own body as the true temple of God's presence in the world (John 2:19–21); and now he ministers forever in the heavenly temple above (Heb 8:5).

(6) *God Gives the King "Wisdom" to Build, Govern, and Teach.* The Lord invited Solomon to make any request of him that he desired, and Solomon asked for the gift of wisdom to govern the kingdom entrusted to him (1 Kings 3:5–12). This greatly pleased the Lord, so much so that he gave the king wealth and long life in addition to wisdom (1 Kings 3:13–14, 28; 4:29). Solomon was given wisdom for building the Temple and for instructing Israel and other nations in the ways of the Lord (1 Kings 4:34; 10:1–10). Several wisdom books of the Old Testament—Proverbs, Ecclesiastes, Song of Solomon, Wisdom of Solomon—are attributed to Solomon. In the New Testament, Jesus is a new Solomon figure and the incarnation of divine Wisdom (1 Cor 1:30). He now instructs the nations and imparts the wisdom and Spirit of God to the world (John 12:7–15).

(7) *The Kingdom is an Everlasting Kingdom.* The kingdom that God establishes with David is everlasting (2 Sam 7:13; Psalm 89:36–37). On the one hand, the dynasty of kings descended from David is the longest lasting dynasty in recorded history, stretching from 1000 to 586 BC. But even four hundred years of unbroken succession falls short of "everlasting." With the fall of Jerusalem in 586 BC, it appears that God's covenant of kingship with David fails. Nevertheless, the prophets encourage the covenant people with the hope that God will restore his kingdom and the messianic son of David will reign. The fulfillment of this hope is announced in the New Testament, as Jesus comes in the line of David, ascends into heaven, and reigns over his everlasting kingdom from the heavenly Jerusalem.

Secondary Features of the Davidic Covenant

(1) *The Queen Mother.* Solomon, the Bible tells us, had multiple wives, but only his mother Bathsheba was queen in his kingdom. Only she was honored with a royal throne (1 Kings 2:19). And this exalted position was reserved for each new queen, who was known in Hebrew as the *gebirah* [geh-vee-ráh]. In the New Testament, Jesus is the royal heir of David, which means that Mary is the royal queen mother in his kingdom.

(2) *The Prime Minister.* The Davidic kingdom also had a government position for a prime minister. The mark of his office is the *keys* of the kingdom, and these symbolize both the *authority* and the *succession* of his office (Isa 22:15–22). In the New Testament, Jesus is the Davidic king who installs Simon Peter as his prime minister and the keeper of the royal keys (Matt 16:19).

(3) *The Todah or Thank Offering.* In the time of David, the traditional thanksgiving sacrifice (Lev 7:11–15) rose to a place of prominence in Israel's temple worship. David wrote many *todah* psalms, which tend to follow a set pattern (e.g., Psalm 50). This gave rise to a spirituality in which the Israelites came to offer their hardships to the Lord in thanksgiving. According to several psalms, grateful praise is the kind of worship that God truly desires from his people (e.g., Psalm 69:30–31). In the New Testament, Jesus makes the Eucharist (a Greek term that means "thanksgiving") the centerpiece of Christian worship.

The Kingdom Established

David prefigures Jesus in many ways, but not in the matter of sin. David, the Bible tells us, lusted after a woman (Bathsheba), committed adultery with her, and then tried to cover up his transgression by arranging for the death of her husband (Uriah). The prophet Nathan confronts David with the Lord's verdict: because of these sins, the sword of divine judgment will never depart from his house, and the child conceived by his adultery will die. At this point, David throws himself on the mercy of God (Psalm 51), marries Bathsheba, and together they bring forth another son, Solomon, who is chosen by God to sit on David's throne.

Early in Solomon's reign, the Lord's three promises in Genesis 12:1–3 reach a new level of fulfillment. Abraham's descendants have acquired *land* and nationhood (1 Kings 4:21); the prospect of a *great name* or royal dynasty has become a reality (2 Sam 7:9); and the promise to bestow *blessings on the world* is a process now begun through the services of Solomon's Temple and the dissemination of Solomon's wisdom (Psalm 72:17). The transition from the Mosaic to the Davidic covenant, from Sinai to Zion, is essentially complete.

The Fall of the Kingdom and the Promise of Restoration

Looking ahead to the founding of a monarchy, Moses places three restrictions on the future kings of Israel: they must not multiply weapons, wives, or wealth for themselves (Deut 17:16–17). Despite his promising start, Solomon soon violates all three limits: he multiplies horses and chariots (*weapons*), he amasses gold and silver on a grand scale (*wealth*), and through an astounding number of marriages he forges political ties with other nations (*wives*). Once Solomon strays from the Lord in his heart, things take a downward turn (1 Kings 11:1–5).

The fallout of these failures is the division of Solomon's kingdom after his death.

Ten northern tribes of Israel break away from Jerusalem and set up a rival kingdom (the kingdom of Israel), leaving only the two southern tribes of Judah and Benjamin to be ruled by the Davidic king (the kingdom of Judah).

The northern kingdom of Israel eventually fell to the Assyrians in 722 BC, at which time the northern tribes went into exile, never to return. The southern kingdom of Judah lasted longer but fell to the Babylonians in 586 BC, at which time the southern tribes went off into seventy years of exile. Unlike the northern tribes, the southern tribes (the "Judeans" or "Jews") returned to the homeland to rebuild the Lord's Temple. Their enemies, however, made life in the land an ongoing struggle.

Even while God's people had a political leader in David and his royal successors, the Lord raised up prophets, anointed by his Spirit, who gave spiritual guidance. Part of their mission was to announce that David's kingdom, though destroyed for a time, would be restored in the Messiah. And this figure would not appear as a conquering hero, leading troops into battle, but as one who will suffer greatly at the hands of others (Isa 53:4–6). The Messiah will offer his life as a sacrifice of atonement for the forgiveness of sins. The prophet Jeremiah explains that God will ratify a "new covenant" that brings his purposes to fulfillment (Jer 31:31–34). Once this new covenant is established, God's plan to gather the whole world into his family will at last be realized.

What We'll Cover in Lesson 11

Themes Covered

❖ The "New Adam" in the garden

❖ Jesus as the "Son of Abraham"

❖ The awaited "New Moses"

❖ The change in the priesthood

❖ The New Passover celebrated and fulfilled

Scripture Verses Read in Lesson 11

❖ Galatians 3:13–14

❖ John 5:39, 46–47

❖ John 6:32–35

Notes

Review Questions

1. In what ways does Jesus bear the covenant curses triggered by Adam and Eve?

_____

_____

_____

_____

2. There are striking similarities between the sacrifice of Isaac and the crucifixion of Jesus. What are the main parallels between the two?

_____

_____

_____

_____

3. What are some of the biblical parallels between Moses and Jesus?

_____

_____

_____

_____

Discussion Questions

1. Can you think of anything in this lesson that you've never considered before, or even heard before? If so, how might this new information impact your relationship with God and others?

_____

_____

_____

_____

2. We've seen that Jesus is prefigured by Adam, Isaac, and Moses. Which of these biblical types do you find most interesting or illuminating? Why?

_____

_____

_____

_____

3. What experiences have you had in sharing the gospel of Jesus Christ with others? What types of reactions have you gotten?

_____

_____

_____

_____

This Lesson's Memory Verse

"Jesus then said to them, 'Truly, truly, I say to you, it was not Moses who gave you the bread from heaven; my Father gives you the true bread from heaven. For the bread of God is that which comes down from heaven, and gives life to the world.' They said to him, 'Lord, give us this bread always.' Jesus said to them, 'I am the bread of life; he who comes to me shall not hunger, and he who believes in me shall never thirst.'"

JOHN 6:32–35

Preparation for the Next Lesson

❖ *A Father Who Keeps His Promises* by Dr. Scott Hahn, ch. 13

THE KINGDOM TRANSFORMED

Review of the Previous Lesson

Salvation history is the story of God making covenants in order to make us his family. Through Jesus, the mediator of the New covenant, all the promises of the Old Testament—especially the covenants made with Adam, Noah, Abraham, Moses, and David—reach their ultimate fulfillment.

The New Adam

The first Adam failed his test of obedience in the garden of Eden. Jesus, the new Adam, undergoes a test of obedience in the garden of Gethsemane, but he prays to his Father: "Your will be done" (Matt 26:42). The damage caused by Adam's failure is undone by Christ's faithfulness.

The curses of the covenant were unleashed by Adam's disobedience: having sinned, the first man found himself naked and ashamed (Gen 3:7–10); his work became a toilsome struggle (Gen 3:17) against thorns and thistles (Gen 3:18) that caused him to sweat (Gen 3:19); and his life was

destined to end in death (Gen 3:19). Jesus bears these Adamic curses, only in a redemptive way: he is stripped naked and forced to endure a shameful death (Matt 27:31); he sweats blood (Luke 22:44); he is crowned with thorns (Matt 27:29); and he surrenders his life in death.

The Son of Abraham

Abraham's obedience in "binding" Isaac calls forth God's oath in Genesis 22:18. In this passage the Lord swears to bless all nations of the world through Abraham's seed. What Abraham did not realize, however, is that the offering of Isaac was prefiguring *how* this divine oath would be fulfilled. He assured his beloved Isaac: "God will provide himself the lamb" (Gen 22:8). It turns out that Abraham obeyed the Lord's command to sacrifice Isaac because he believed that God could raise his son from the dead, if necessary (Heb 11:19).

The New Testament identifies Jesus as "the son of Abraham" (Matt 1:1) and the "only-begotten Son" of the Father (John 3:16) who offers his life to bring blessing to the world. Like Isaac, he hauls the wood for his sacrifice up the mountain, and there, on the heights of Moriah, God provides the Lamb that Abraham had spoken about (Gen 22:8). On the third day, the Father's beloved Son is raised from the dead, much like Isaac was returned alive to his father after a three-day ordeal (Gen 22:4). In these ways, Jesus fulfills God's oath to bless all nations through Abraham's seed (Gal 3:13–14).

The New Moses

Parallels between Jesus and Moses are numerous. Both are born when a ruthless king seeks the death of Hebrew male children ("the slaughter of the innocents"). Both find refuge for a time in Egypt. Both return to their birthplace after the death of the ruthless king. And both come out of Egypt, pass through water, and follow God's leading into the wilderness.

Ministry. Jesus fasts for forty days and nights in the wilderness, just as Moses took no food or drink for forty days on Sinai. Jesus is tested for forty days in the wilderness, just as Israel underwent forty years of testing in the wilderness. In the midst of his testing, Jesus rebukes the devil by citing the passages from Deuteronomy 6–8 where Moses looks back on Israel's failures in the wilderness.

Following his fast, Jesus begins his ministry by announcing the new law, setting up the standards of the New Covenant in the Sermon on the Mount (Matt 5–7). Likewise, following his fast, Moses brought the old law, setting up the standards of the Old Covenant from Mount Sinai (Exod 20–23). This law is not abolished by Jesus but fulfilled. In fact, Jesus *internalizes* and *intensifies* the Mosaic law. To take an example: Moses forbids adultery, but Jesus forbids both the act of adultery and the sins of the heart associated with it, including lust (Matt 5:31–32).

Signs and Miracles. According to the Gospel of John, the first miracle or "sign" that Jesus performed was turning water in stone jars into wine at the wedding feast at Cana (John 2:1–11). According to the Book of Exodus, the first miracle or sign that Moses performed in Egypt was turning water into blood, even water in "vessels of stone" (Exod 7:19). Similarly, Jesus performed miracles of multiplying bread to feed the multitudes (John 6:5–14), recalling how Israel under Moses was fed with miraculous bread from heaven (Exod 16:2–30). Ultimately, Jesus himself is the true bread from heaven (John 6:32, 35).

Friends and Co-Workers. Both Jesus and Moses invite others to join in their work of leading the people of God. Jesus choses twelve apostles (Luke 6:13–16); Moses selects twelve tribal leaders to gather

information about the Promised Land (Num 13:1–16). Jesus appoints seventy disciples to preach the gospel (Luke 10:1); Moses appoints seventy elders to help bear the burden of leadership (Num 11:16–25). Jesus has an inner circle of disciples—Peter, James, and John; Moses has an inner circle of priestly collaborators—Aaron, Nabad, and Abihu (Exod 24:1).

Transfigured on a Mountain. When Jesus is transfigured on the mountain, he is revealed as a new Moses. He takes three companions with him (Luke 9:28); his face shines with the glory of God (Luke 9:29); and he speaks about his "exodus" or departure (Luke 9:31). All of this recalls how Moses took three companions up Mount Sinai (Exod 24:1); his face shone with the glory of God (Exod 34:29–35); and God had chosen him to lead Israel out of Egypt (Exod 3:10).

The New Passover

The Gospel accounts of the Last Supper show us that Jesus transforms the Jewish Passover into the Christian Eucharist (Matt 26:26–29). The Passover, long a memorial of Israel's departure from slavery (Exod 12:14), is now made a memorial "in remembrance" of the new salvation accomplished by Jesus (Luke 22:19). The Old Covenant was sealed by the blood of the covenant shed at Sinai (Exod 24:8), and now the New Covenant is sealed by the "blood of the covenant" that Jesus sheds on the cross and makes present in the cup (Matt 26:28).

Jesus's fulfillment of the Passover is especially clear in the Gospel of John. Jesus is condemned to crucifixion at the sixth hour—the time when Passover lambs are being prepared for sacrifice in the Temple (John 19:14). The soldiers who crucify Jesus decline to break his legs—a detail that connects with the law of Passover, which forbids breaking the bones of the pascal lamb (John 19:32–36; Exod 12:46). Jesus is stripped of a seamless garment, which recalls the seamless vestment worn by the high priest of Israel (John 19:23; Exod 28:32). Lastly, the soldiers offer Jesus a drink that is lifted up on a hyssop branch—the kind of branch that was used to smear lamb's blood on their homes at the first Passover (John 19:29; Exod 12:21–23).

All of this shows that Jesus accomplishes a new Passover, and, further, that Jesus's actions at the Last Supper and his offering on Calvary are inseparable. They are not two different sacrifices; they are one and the same. What begins at the Passover meal in the Upper Room is completed on the cross. The blood that is "poured out" into the cup at the Last Supper is the same blood that is poured out of Jesus's crucified body. And this is a sacrificial act, recalling how the blood of animal offerings was poured out by the priests of Israel (Exod 29:12; Lev 4:7).

Yet the work of salvation, rooted in the death of Jesus, remains incomplete without his rising from the dead. Our salvation is accomplished through his dying *and* rising, as Saint Paul indicates in Romans 4:24–25. The miracle of Easter is more than a dead man resuscitated or an innocent man vindicated. When Jesus is resurrected to new life, his humanity is glorified and even divinized (CCC 651–655). In short, God's covenant plan reaches its ultimate fulfillment in the Messiah's resurrection (1 Cor 15:20–22; 42–45).

☻What We'll Cover in Lesson 11

Themes Covered

❖ Jesus as the Son of David

❖ The *todah* fulfilled in the Eucharist

❖ The restoration of the kingdom

❖ The heavenly Jerusalem

Scripture Verses Read in Lesson 12

❖ Matthew 4:23

❖ Matthew 12:42

❖ Matthew 16:18–19

❖ Isaiah 22:20–22

❖ 1 Kings 1:38–40

❖ Luke 22:24–27

❖ Acts 15:13–19

❖ Hebrews 12:22–24, 28

Notes

Review Questions

1. What is the dominant theme that stands out in Jesus's preaching? What is the connection between this theme and the covenants of the Old Testament?

_____

_____

_____

_____

2. In what ways does the kingdom of God proclaimed by Jesus surpass the ancient kingdom of David and Solomon?

_____

_____

_____

_____

3. What does it mean to say that the Eucharist is the new Passover? How are the Last Supper and the cross related to one another?

_____

_____

_____

_____

Discussion Questions

1. Can you think of anything in this lesson that you've never considered before, or even heard before? If so, how might this new information impact your relationship with God and others?

_____

_____

_____

_____

2. How might what you've learned in these last two lessons impact the way you view the holy sacrifice of the Mass?

_____

_____

_____

_____

3. Practically speaking, what are some ways that you can tell others what you learned in this study? Suppose you only had three minutes to invite someone to a Bible study. What might you say to persuade them?

_____

_____

_____

_____

This Lesson's Memory Verse

> *"'And I tell you, you are Peter, and on this rock I will build my Church, and the gates of Hades shall not prevail against it. I will give you the keys of the kingdom of heaven, and whatever you bind on earth shall be bound in heaven, and whatever you loose on earth shall be loosed in heaven.' Then he strictly charged the disciples to tell no one that he was the Christ."*
>
>
>
> MATTHEW 16:18–19

Appendix – Common Prayers

Our Father
Our Father, who art in heaven,
Hallowed be thy name.
Thy kingdom come.
Thy will be done, on earth as it is in heaven.
Give us this day our daily bread.
And forgive us our trespasses,
as we forgive those who trespass against us.
And lead us not into temptation,
but deliver us from evil.
Amen.

Hail Mary
Hail Mary, full of grace,
The Lord is with thee.
Blessed art thou among women,
and blessed is the fruit of thy womb, Jesus.
Holy Mary, mother of God,
pray for us sinners now
and at the hour of death.
Amen.

Come Holy Spirit
Come, Holy Spirit, fill the hearts of thy faithful and enkindle in them the fire of thy love.
V. Send forth thy Spirit and they shall be created.
R. And thou shalt renew the face of the earth.
Let us pray. O God, who didst instruct the hearts of the faithful by the light of the Holy Spirit, grant us the same Spirit to be truly wise, and ever rejoice in his consolation. Through Christ our Lord.
Amen.

Glory Be
Glory be to the Father,
and to the Son,
and to the Holy Spirit.
As it was in the beginning,
is now, and ever shall be;
world without end.
Amen.

Image Attributions

Front Cover: Gaudenzio Ferrari | *Christ rising from the Tomb* | 1530–1546 | National Gallery, London, United Kingdom

Page 5: Peter Paul Rubens | *St. Thomas* (detail) | 1612–1613 | Prado National Museum, Madrid, Spain

Page 11: Rembrandt van Rijn | *An Old Woman Reading, Probably the Prophetess Hannah* (detail) | 1631 | Rijksmuseum, Amsterdam, Netherlands

Page 12: Jan Wildens | *Landscape with Christ and His Disciples on the Road to Emmaus* (detail) | 1640s | Hermitage Museum, Saint Petersburg, Russia

Page 13: Marinus van Reymerswaele | *St Jerome in His Study* (detail) | 1541 | Prado National Museum, Madrid, Spain

Page 19: Francesco Bassano | *God Reprimanding Adam* | c.1570 | Prado National Museum, Madrid, Spain

Page 20: Rembrandt van Rijn | *The Apostle Paul* | c.1657 | National Gallery of Art, Washington, D.C., United States of America

Page 21: Peter Paul Rubens | *Saint Peter* | 1610–1612 | Prado National Museum, Madrid, Spain

Page 27: Francesco Albani | *Adam and Eve Expelled from Paradise* (detail) | Date Unknown | Palace of Versailles, Versailles, France

Page 28: Jan Brueghel II and Workshop | *Paradise Landscape with the Creation of the Animals* (detail)

Page 29: Jan Brueghel the Elder | *The Garden of Eden with the Fall of Man* (detail) | 1612 | Doria Pamphilj Gallery, Rome, Italy

Page 35: Lodewijk Tieling | *The Ark* | c.1700 | Metropolitan Museum of Art, New York City, New York, United States of America

Page 36: Artist Unknown | *Adam and Eve* | 16th century | Hermitage Museum, Saint Petersburg, Russia

Page 37: Caravaggio | *Madonna and Child with St. Anne* (detail) | c.1605–1606 | Galleria Borghese, Rome, Italy

Page 43: Rembrandt van Rijn | *Sacrifice of Isaac* | 1635 | Hermitage Museum, Saint Petersburg, Russia

Page 44: Palma il Giovane | *Cain and Abel* (detail) | c.1603 | Kunsthistorisches Museum, Vienna, Austria

Page 46: Ivan Stepanovitch Ksenofontov | *Noah Damning Ham* | 19th-century

Page 53: C.W. Eckersberg | *The Israelites Resting after the Crossing of the Red Sea* | 1815 | Statens Museum for Kunst, Copenhagen, Denmark

Page 54: Peter Paul Rubens | *The Meeting of Abraham and Melchizedek* (detail) | 1625 | National Gallery of Art, Washington, D.C., United States of America

Page 55: Gainsborough Dupont | *Abraham and Isaac* (detail) | c.1787 | Museum of the Shenandoah Valley, Winchester, Virginia, United States of America

Page 56: David Teniers the Younger | *Abraham's Sacrifice* (detail) | 1653 | Kunsthistorisches Museum, Vienna, Austria

Page 63: Krzysztof Lubieniecki | *Moses Strikes Water from the Stone* (detail) | 1714 | National Museum, Warsaw, Poland

Page 64: Domenichino | *Landscape with Moses and the Burning Bush* | 1610–1616 | Metropolitan Museum of Art, New York City, New York, United State of America

Page 65: Rembrandt van Rijn | *Moses Smashing the Tablets of the Law* | 1659 | Gemäldegalerie, Berlin, Germany

Page 71: Guercino | *King David* | 1651 | Spencer House, London, England

Page 72: Claes Moeyaert | *Sacrifice of Jeroboam* (detail) | 1641

Page 73: Ferdinand Bol | *Moses Descends from Mount Siniai with the Ten Commandments* | 1641 | Cantor Arts Center, Stanford, California

Page 79: Frans de Grebber | *King David in Prayer* | c. 1635–1640 | Museum Catharijneconvent, Utrecht, Netherlands.

Page 80: Peter Paul Rubens David | *Slaying Goliath* | c.1616 | Norton Simon Museum, Pasadena, California, United States of America

Page 81: Hendrick ter Brugghen | *King David Playing the Harp* (detail) | 1628 | National Museum, Warsaw, Poland

Page 87: Peter Paul Rubens | *Supper at Emmaus* | c.1635–c.1640 | Prado National Museum, Madrid, Spain

Page 88: Ignacio de Ries | *King David* (detail) | c.1650 | Prado National Museum, Madrid, Spain

Page 89: Jan de Bray | *David Playing the Harp* (detail) | 1670

Page 90: Cornelis de Vos | *The Anointing of Solomon* (detail) | c.1630s | Kunsthistorisches Museum, Vienna, Austria

Page 97: Bartolomé Esteban Murillo | *The Lord's Resurrection* (detail) | c.1655 | Royal Academy of Fine Arts of San Fernando, Madrid, Spain

Page 98: Julius Schnorr von Carolsfeld | *The Wedding Feast at Cana* (detail) | 1819 | Hamburger Kunsthalle, Hamburg, Germany

Page 99: Juan de Juanes | *The Last Supper* (detail) | c.1562 | Prado National Museum, Madrid, Spain